*Coping with*
# YOUR HANDICAPPED CHILD

Dr Judy Bury, the General Editor of this series, has worked in general practice and family planning for many years. She writes regularly on medical topics, and has a particular interest in self-help approaches to health care.

*Coping with*
# YOUR HANDICAPPED CHILD

ANDRINA E McCORMACK,
MA DipEd MSc DipSpEd

With a Foreword by
BRIAN RIX, CBE

Chambers

Published by W & R Chambers Ltd Edinburgh

Illustrations by David Wilson

ISBN 0 550 20507 1

**British Library Cataloguing in Publication Data**

McCormack, Andrina E.
    Coping with your handicapped child.
    1. Handicapped children — Care and treatment
    I. Title
    362.4'088054        HQ773.6
    ISBN 0-550-20507-1

Printed by Clark Constable, Edinburgh, London, Melbourne

# Contents

Andrina E McCormack works as educationist (mental health) for the Scottish Health Education Group where she co-ordinates the production of health education, much of it concerned with disability, including information for parents and relatives, and campaigns to promote good social attitudes. She worked in special education as a teacher for over five years, and is still heavily involved in research into social skills and mentally handicapped children. Now living in Edinburgh, she holds degrees from Edinburgh, Dundee and London universities.

The author would like to thank the Scottish Sports Association for the Disabled for the use of the illustration from their booklet of the same title, which appears on p 87; and acknowledges reference to *Special Educational Needs* published by HMSO 1978, *Social Trends No 13 1983* published by the Government Statistical Service, and *Popular Television and School Children* published by the Department of Education and Science 1983.

# Foreword

I wish a book like this one had been available in 1951, when my wife and I were suffering the agonies which all parents of a newly-diagnosed handicapped child have to endure. Our first baby, Shelley, had been born with Down's Syndrome — they called it mongolism then — and we were absolutely devastated. All the advice we were given in our state of shock came from the paediatrician at the hospital where Shelley was born. His view of our daughter's future prospects was bleak indeed. 'Put her in a home and forget all about her', he said. If any alternatives existed, nobody told us about them.

Since then, the quality and quantity of help offered to handicapped people and their families has improved tremendously, but many parents are still not receiving all the information they need to help them make vital decisions about their child's future and take advantage of all the services and facilities designed to meet their special needs. Parents suffering from stress may find it difficult to absorb verbal advice and be reluctant to ask for it to be repeated. There is a definite need for written reference material which they can consult at any time and which will also encourage them to turn to the various sources of assistance when necessary.

This book could be read through from cover to cover by new parents who want to build up a comprehensive picture of life with a child with a mental or physical handicap. Others will find it useful to read one topic or chapter at a time. Its sensible and sensitive approach, which considers the needs of entire families, rather than those of the handicapped child in isolation, will be widely welcomed.

Brian Rix CBE MA DU(Essex)
Secretary-General
MENCAP,
Royal Society for Mentally Handicapped Children & Adults
1985

# 1. Starting Out

## An Initial Word

Nobody ever plans to have a handicapped baby, but it does happen. Nobody ever plans that their child becomes disabled through illness or accident, but that happens too.

'Disability' means lots of different things to lots of different people. In theory there are three terms which have different meanings. These are

*impairment*, where a person has a defective limb, organ or mechanism of the body, or is missing all or part of a limb.

*disability* (or *disablement*), where there is a loss or reduction in what a person can do.

*handicap*, where a person is restricted or disadvantaged by his disability.

To most people however, disability, handicap and impairment all mean the same thing, and are used interchangeably. Whether this is right or wrong cannot be discussed here and at the end of the day those people — parents, professionals and carers — who are involved with disability have more practical considerations to concern themselves with than theoretical categorisation. It is all too easy for people to categorise children and adults with handicap into specific types. In some ways this can be helpful — the needs of a physically disabled child may be vastly different from those of a child with mental handicap. Each child is different, and each is affected in various individual ways by even the same kind of disability. Nevertheless, different disabling conditions share a commonality of approach, support services and benefits, so this book deals with children with difficulties of all kinds rather than identifying any specific type of handicap.

It is all too easy to assume that the mother of a handicapped child is the person who will take most responsibility. But *Coping with Your Handicapped Child* has been written as much for fathers, for those who are single parents, and for those who are separated or divorced parents. Whatever his situation, a father is as important as a mother for any child.

This book aims to give as much information as possible about services available, benefits, and people to help. There are many aids for disabled children, but these are so specific to individual needs, and indeed are being developed and sophisticated at such a rapid rate, that only general reference is made to them, with the advice to speak to medical consultants, a family doctor, social worker or health visitor for more details. No book can give all the answers, but *Coping with Your Handicapped Child* also aims to try and raise some issues which many people see as important. Many issues are raised several times in different contexts throughout the book. Disability is not a subject which can be compartmentalised, or treated as a scientific or behavioural discipline. Disability is about *people*, not just adults who have learned to cope, but babies and young children who are not 'cases' or 'patients' but individual and developing personalities.

*Coping with Your Handicapped Child* is in six parts. 'An Initial Word' introduces the book, and examines the reactions of parents and other people on hearing that a child is disabled in some way. 'Your Special Child' deals with the child growing up, going to school, assessment procedures, and some of the issues which parents should face up to early on, and which apply to children after they leave school. 'Family Matters' looks at the place of the handicapped child in the family, the effect on other siblings and the family as a whole, and includes a section on financial benefits which are available to ease any strain on the family budget. Throughout both these sections, emphasis is placed on the necessity to concentrate on your child's abilities rather than his disabilities. By encouraging him to do what he can to the best of his ability, you are building self-confidence and self-worth. You have to *think ability, not disability*.

'Other People' details statutory and voluntary services which are there to support and help parents with a handicapped child, and also looks at society's attitudes to disability. Many people, through lack of knowledge, fear or embarrassment, have very negative attitudes to people who are disabled and it is up to people who are directly concerned to try in whatever way possible to change this. Such negative attitudes influence professional people who after all are part of the general public too. As a result, services for handicapped people in practice suffer a fairly low priority rating. Services in many areas are patchy and can vary substantially from one vicinity to another.

The final two sections, 'Finding Out More' and 'Looking Ahead', offer further information and hope.

# Being Told

All babies are special in some way. Special to their parents and families, special because they are all new people coming into the world, special because of their talents or their personalities. Some babies are born 'special' babies because of some difficulty or disability they have and some children become 'special' children through illness or accident. The parents of these 'special' children will experience happiness and joy in their children just as other parents will in theirs. Like other parents too they will have problems and difficulties bringing up their children, although the difficulties may be different in many ways.

Parents have children for lots of different reasons: to show their love for each other, to build a family unit, to carry on a family name; or it may be that a baby is unplanned. Whatever the reason, parents plan or hope for a healthy happy child, who will grow up to be a healthy adult taking his or her place in the world.

So when a doctor confirms that the baby has some kind of problem or difficulty, parents may be stunned, disappointed, even angry or bitter. Parents have said

.... 'I didn't want to see her at all for the first few days.'

.... 'We had such a nice family. We just kept asking "Why us?" '

.... 'I was glad my husband knew already. I didn't want to tell him.'

3

.... 'I knew right away there was something wrong. The nurse kept saying "It'll be all right, dear." '

Even when a disability is not identified until a child is older many parents have suffered suspicions that all was not well, so while they may even feel some relief at dealing with hard facts instead of vague worries, it is still hard to face up to what is in effect the reality of the unknown.

.... 'I didn't know much about mental handicap, and didn't really understand what would happen.'

.... 'I had a horrible feeling something was wrong, but I wasn't sure that I wanted to find out what it was.'

.... 'I found it almost impossible to face the fact that because I had married Richard, we had condemned a little boy to a life in a wheelchair.'

The person who has to break the news to the parents, generally a doctor in hospital, has a difficult and unenviable task. Some parents complain, with good cause, that they were told badly of their child's disability, perhaps by a junior doctor with little experience of dealing sensitively with people, or by someone who gave them little information, support or hope for the future. Some parents complain that they were not told at all and, while this can happen, many people forget that they have been told in an attempt to cope more easily with their reactions to the situation.

Much of the information given at this time will be misheard or forgotten because of the anxiety of the situation. Parents should seriously consider going back to their doctor with a list of questions which they want to go over again, or questions which have presented themselves as they have got over their initial reactions. Many people are reluctant to 'bother' the doctor but most professionals would rather clear up any doubts or misunderstandings early rather than later. Some questions of course cannot be answered, and professionals, however knowledgeable, do not have the power to see into the future or play God. Much of children's progress and development depends on parents encouraging them as early as possible to develop their abilities rather than concentrating on their disabilities. Professional staff cannot necessarily anticipate what parents need or want to know. They have to be asked for information, sometimes two or three times, before parents will feel happy that they have the right or satisfactory answer to their questions. It is the right of the parents to ask, and the duty of the professional services to answer to the best of their ability — the services are there for people, not the other way round.

One important question which many parents of a severely handicapped child consider immediately is that of whether they ought to put their child into residential care. Some parents do so immediately because they feel unable to cope emotionally or practically in caring for their child. If parents are considering early residential care, the decision should not be taken lightly or in the heat of the moment. Some children can benefit from being with other children with similar problems, under the care and attention of professional staff. Parents have to weigh up the effects of bringing up a handicapped child on themselves, individuals with a right to a life that they are happy living. They may worry that the care they would give their child would be inadequate or inappropriate. They may feel that it would put too great a strain on their relationship, or have a detrimental effect on their other children. Some people think that by placing their child in residential care they are admitting failure, or letting their child down. They worry about what other people will think of them. And yet it can take even more courage to make a decision like this, and is the right course of action for many people. Those parents who decide to care for their child themselves will almost certainly come up against difficulties that other parents do not face. With appropriate support and advice from professional staff, however, they can very successfully give loving care to children at home, amongst their family and friends.

## Telling the relatives

Once parents have been told that their child is handicapped or disabled they may face the problem of telling relatives and friends.

.... 'They were so looking forward to their first grandchild. I couldn't bear to tell them'.

.... 'I wondered how people would react. Just how do you go about saying "Oh, by the way...."'

Passing on news like this is never easy. Many parents find that relatives are unwilling or unable to accept the news, and treat what can never be 'cured' as an illness which may be recovered from. One mother tells of her aunt who, after several years, still asks 'And is Thomas better now?'. Many people cope with the situation by totally ignoring the handicap, as if by doing so the problem will miraculously disappear. Some go to the other extreme and lavish so much time and effort on the disabled child, that a parent or other children feel not only left out but resentful, as with one lady who says angrily 'My mother practically ignored me when she came to visit. Her first question was always "How's Rob?". She never asked how I was, or whether I was all right.'

However relatives react to the news, it is important for everybody's sake to recognise that emotions can run high about handicap, and stresses and strains can be increased at a time when parents least need pressure. Talking openly — and calmly — about the nature of your child's handicap is to everybody's immediate and long term benefit.

## Coming to terms with the news

In many areas there are parents' groups which can help parents understand their feelings and come to terms with their child's disability. Many people feel that they are not ready to talk with a group of people, even those who have been through the same situation. Doctors and ministers can be useful counsellors where appropriate. A few health centres do have counsellors attached but these are at present not very common. Parents can turn however to the Samaritans when they feel that things are pretty desperate. Their phone numbers are listed in the directory under S. Coming to terms with news like this may take quite a long time, and parents may go through a long grieving period. It is vital for your complete wellbeing not to bottle your feelings up, but to admit that you may be emotional. Only that way will you be able to face up to the future in a positive and practical way.

# 2. Your Special Child

## Up to Five

The early years of a child's life are the most crucial in laying the foundations for future growth and development. During these formative years a child lays down the basis of *motor (movement) skills*, everything from picking up a tiny object to moving around; *cognitive skills*, thinking, learning, reasoning; *social and emotional skills*, smiling, recognising people, showing feelings; and *communication skills*, communicating with others through signs and gestures, and perhaps speech and language.

### *Early assessment*

Because these years are so vital, it is important that any worries you have about your child's progress be investigated. Early assessment, usually by a children's specialist (paediatrician) and then by other specialists, can ensure that as much as possible is done — at the right time — to help a disabled child develop to his best potential. Many professionals talk about 'sensitive' or 'critical' periods in a child's development, times when he or she is particularly ready to learn a new skill. So that if you try and teach a child something before he is ready, he will not be able to learn it — in other words, he will not run before he can walk. Parents and supporting professionals must make sure they do not miss the time when the child is most ready to learn, since this could result in a child being further disabled. Health visitors, paediatricians and in fortunate areas home-visiting teachers will be able, in consultation with parents, to advise on their child's progress.

### *Learning life*

It may seem surprising to many adults that little human beings work harder in the first few years of their life than they do at any other time. Constantly coming into contact with new surroundings, new people and at the same time having to begin to learn living skills, new babies are always processing new information. This is one reason why they sleep so much. During sleep, we sort out and categorise new information so that it can be easily retrieved when we need it. As we grow older we need less sleep since we are not learning as many new things.

## *Play*

All children learn about their environment through a variety of different mechanisms. One important way of learning is through play with people, with objects, and with other children. For disabled children play is particularly important since they may not pick things up in passing the way other children do. It seems strange that children have to be encouraged to play but, because it is such a powerful way of learning, parents can use play to stimulate different functions and skills according to their child's handicap.

By playing with your child's fingers and toes, with his nose, arms and legs, touching or tickling them, you are stimulating muscles and nerves which might otherwise not be exercised very much. You are also stimulating 'body awareness' or helping your child learn where all the bits of his body are in relation to each other. For many children with a disability, neck muscles can be a particular problem — in fact a floppy head can be the first indicator of a problem in a child. By rubbing the back of your baby's neck, by gently touching his chin, to encourage him to keep it up, you are helping the muscles to strengthen and send messages to the brain to keep the head upright.

A mobile hanging near where the baby lies is also good for attracting visual and auditory attention, and you can encourage 'visual tracking', the skill of following an object visually, by shining a torch and moving it round so that your child will follow the light source. Similarly, tinkling a bell from behind or to the side of your baby will help him learn to locate sounds.

There are many toys, games and activity centres available from toy shops which are designed to develop different skills and functions. However, many of these are very expensive and you may find that having spent quite a lot of money, the toy is not suitable for your child or indeed he or she simply may not like it or not be interested in it. Most parents can tell stories recalling similar instances to that of the child who was surrounded by expensive Christmas presents and who was engrossed playing with a mothball which had fallen out of the pocket of his doting aunt's fur coat. In most local areas there is a Toy Library which will lend out different toys for a month or so at a time. There is no fee for this service and parents are not responsible for breakage or damage. Your local library or Citizens' Advice Bureau should have information about the Toy Library nearest you.

Toys and games are useful in helping your child develop new skills, but they are not the only things that children can play with. A box full of everyday objects — plastic food-boxes, a plastic whisk, a rubber ball, string, a hair band, and anything else you can think of — can be a great source of fun for your child. Safety of course comes first and you should discard sharp or breakable objects, or anything which could catch a child's fingers. You can buy safety mirrors from most toy shops.

Remember however that play is just that — it should be fun and creative, not an intensive learning situation where the child feels pressurised into achieving a goal set by an adult. There is a fine line between encouragement and enforcement. There is a temptation when a child is doing well to push — just that little bit more — and it can be counterproductive. Children know themselves just what their capacity for interest and enthusiasm is. They need encouragement too though in the form of a smile, a cuddle, a little pat on the shoulder or back — or something that they really like, being tickled, or having you blow gently in their face or in their ear.

## *Rewards and reinforcement*

Throughout our lives we all need encouragement and 'positive reinforcement' to continue persevering while learning a new task, or to endorse our feelings of satisfaction at having done something well. A cuddle or a smile at the right time can tell a child that he is doing well and spur him on to greater things.

Some parents however seem to believe that a hug is not enough, that children need a sweet or chocolate to prove that they have done well. Some parents even over-feed their disabled youngsters in an attempt to compensate for the fact that they are disabled. By using food for the wrong purposes parents can set their children on the road to physical ill health in later life, as well as perhaps making them psychologically dependent on food for emotional reasons — many people with weight problems eat when they are tense or anxious, when they need to be comforted in some way or when they are on a high, having done something well. This is not to say that all sweeties are bad and that children should not be allowed to eat between meals. We all deserve a treat now and then. But raisins or cornflakes or a piece of fruit can frequently be substituted — not necessarily totally — for the high sugar, low nutrient confections available in shops.

## *Breaking things down*

Parents are the experts as far as their own children are concerned. Because you are probably with your child more often than any other person is, you will be able to test out whether your youngster is ready to try and feed or dress himself or go to the toilet. But Rome was not built in a day nor is any skill developed overnight. Nobody suddenly learns to speak or walk; it is a slow construction and piecing together of a massive amount of information surrounding a child all day. You can help by breaking down a task into its separate steps — perhaps even going to the bother of writing them down for reference — and working with your child on each step. For instance the 'simple' act of picking up a spoon requires several different actions all coming together.

1. Identify which spoon is to be picked up
2. Lift hand and direct it generally towards the spoon
3. Open fingers and thumb in readiness to grasp
4. Touch spoon
5. Grasp spoon
6. Lift spoon up

This may seem a simplistic and basic way to tackle a trivial everyday act of lifting up a spoon. But many children have difficulty at each one of these six stages and, by practising each one separately where necessary, a child does not have to try to do too much all at once. Any task can be broken down into such functional components, and a child can work on each step, gaining confidence and skill slowly but surely. For instance pulling on a jersey requires a person to first pick up the garment, open up the bottom of it, put it over the head, pull it down over the face, put one arm in, then the other, and finally to pull the jersey down to the waist. Each step should be taken at a time and may require lots of time and patience.

It may be easier for a parent to put a child's clothes on for him or to feed him, but it is no favour to the child and indeed may damage the possibility of his developing those skills in future.

## Learning to live

Learning how to put clothes on, eat and go to the toilet can be difficult for even the fittest and brightest children. At the same time they may be learning how to walk and talk, how to live with other people, and how to recognise their world around them. Children with a disability may encounter even more difficulty because of the various effects of their impairment.

Children with poor muscle control may have difficulty in placing objects accurately. They may experience 'intention tremor', shaky hands, just at the moment they direct their hand to do something. If there are no clear physical reasons for this, relaxation exercises can sometimes help and a physiotherapist should be able to advise on appropriate techniques. One thing which will not help a child who has this problem is to become self-conscious or embarrassed by any problems he or she may be experiencing. No matter how mentally or physically handicapped a child may be, he will quickly notice that someone is watching him and pick up feelings of disapproval or criticism, and while these are appropriate in some circumstances, they can be destructive if nothing can be done to solve the problem.

Children who are mentally handicapped may forget very easily what you have told them many times. By showing children what you want them to do, you will make it easier for them to understand and remember. There is an old Chinese proverb:

> I hear and I forget
> I see and I remember
> I do and I understand.

You have to be clear too in what you say and how you say it. A mentally impaired child will probably not perceive 'Would you shut the door?' as a command, but as a question which requires an answer rather than action. The same child would understand clearly 'Go and shut the door' without feeling any resentment. What may seem directive to an adult will be a useful and clear communication to a child.

The ability to move about is one of the most basic skills a human being develops. Even if a child will never be independently mobile he will still need to be aware of the environment and the relationship 'in space' of one object, including himself, to another in order to crawl or to get around in a wheelchair or with a walking aid. Children can be developing such awareness if they are allowed to lie on the floor unhampered by clothes or blankets or if put in a baby bouncing cradle where they can see everything going on around them. By encouraging any kind of movement early on you are helping your child to strengthen muscles, practise different physical movements and build muscle movement patterns for the future.

## *Aids*

Everyone would agree that disabled children should be encouraged to do as much as possible for themselves. However, children with certain specific difficulties may find that using a particular kind of aid can help them do something which they would not normally be able to cope with. Many aids are available to help children with poor grasp control, including cutlery with large grip handles, specially-designed cups, and gadgets to help fasten buttons on clothing. For those with toileting problems, incontinence pads and disposable nappies are available from the National Health Service. For the older child who cannot walk extra-large push-chairs are available from the statutory services. Your health visitor or health centre should be able to give you more information on all of these. New and more sophisticated aids are being developed every day. There are electronic aids to help people communicate through a voice synthesiser, and to help them with many everyday tasks. The best way to keep up to date with these is through newsletters and publications from the voluntary organisation concerned with your child's disability. These are listed in the section entitled 'Finding Out More'.

## *Keeping in touch*

Many parents of handicapped children recall that as babies their children were particularly good or particularly grumpy. Whichever extreme your child may fall into — most babies are not one or the other — it is important that you establish a good strong relationship with each other as early as possible.

Because of neonatal problems, illness, or prematurity, many handicapped children do not begin to get to know their parents until they are days, weeks or even months old. Therefore the

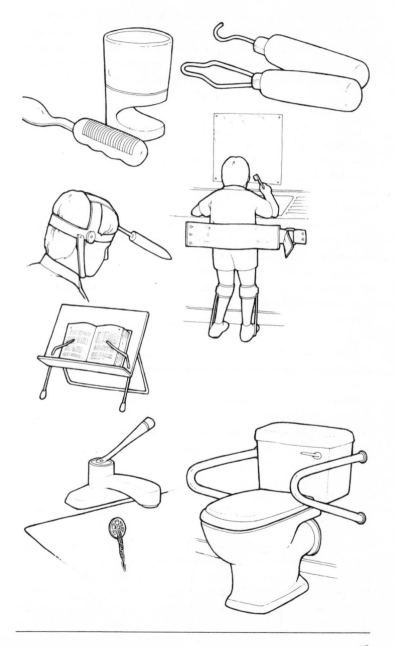

natural mechanisms for establishing a bond are disturbed, and have to be closely and intensively worked on. Parents of very quiet passive babies may be tempted to leave the baby even when he or she is awake because they are relieved to have time to themselves. Parents of very grumpy babies may be only too glad to have a respite from the tension and stress that constant crying can engender. However, good parent-child bonding is essential for emotional health later on, and parents of handicapped children should recognise that they may have to work a bit harder than others on this. Both quiet and noisy babies will benefit from close involvement with other people. By stimulating their interest you will focus their attention and help them become more aware of the world around them.

The relationship a child has with a parent or a carer is his first experience of communication with other people and as such influences the skills in communication and personal relationships which he will develop and display in the future. Children and parents interact or 'have conversations' long before the child can speak, by looking and smiling at each other and by the parent responding to a child's gurgling noises. This is now considered to be an instinctive response, designed by mother nature to encourage those who can speak to do so, in order that the child can experience and hear as much language as possible to learn it. However there is a risk that a handicapped child may be overwhelmed or flooded with the amount of language he is hearing. It can be difficult to achieve the right balance especially if a child is particularly quiet, when parents might feel that talking seems a waste of time because the child seems to understand very little. But attention like this always draws parents and children together. It may be that as parents of a handicapped child, especially one with a mental or sensory handicap, you have to slow down a little to give your child time to respond to a smile or a hug.

We communicate in lots of different ways, not just through language. Indeed many disabled children will never communicate by the use of the spoken word. Eye contact is vital for the basis of any communication, and this is reflected in the phrases which appear in our language — 'I couldn't look myself in the eye', '... he looked deep into her eyes...', '... she looked him straight in the eye...'. Many disabled children need special encouragement to make eye contact and this should start very early on. This does not mean that a baby should always be in eye to eye contact with someone. He may turn away because something else is of interest, or because he needs a pause or a rest from the interaction. Touch is also a very important sense in our communication process. It can be used to attract a handicapped child's attention, by running your finger down his cheek, or by patting his hand, or his lips, if you want him to speak. At the other extreme, by loving hugs and kisses, touch can express deep love and affection. Stroking and patting a child's skin, arms and legs, and body can help the child develop a sense of body awareness. Massage too can help by stimulating blood vessels and muscles.

## *The world outside*

As a toddler grows up his first major step into the outside world is to nursery or school. In order to make the transition less traumatic, parents should take every opportunity to let their child come into contact with new people to accustom him to any strange reactions he may encounter due to his handicap. It also builds confidence and security and helps when a child is 'left' at nursery or school.

Although there are a few special nurseries, many ordinary nursery schools are becoming increasingly willing to take in a handicapped child, the major criterion being that the child is toilet-trained, at least to the point where only the odd accident occurs. Mixing with ordinary toddlers at this stage is beneficial for all concerned and should be encouraged. The head of the local nursery school will advise on whether there is a place suitable for your disabled child.

Whether a child has been to nursery or not, at five years old all children go to school. This can be a particularly difficult time for parents of handicapped children, since they have to face what can be the harsh reality of their child's disability. When a child is small parents can pretend, or ignore a disability. Many disabled children are considered 'cute' because they are more helpless than ordinary toddlers. But going to school marks the time when a disability may be emphasised by the fact that the child is going to a different school from other children, or is being bussed to school in special transport. Parents, especially mothers, may find that their day is empty without the work caused by the child's being at home. But it is the natural course of events that children grow up and move away from their parents, who for their own and their child's health and welfare have to learn to let go. Mothers have said....

.... 'Looking after Ben was a full-time job. When he went to school I was finished the housework by half-past-ten and didn't know what to do for the rest of the day.'

.... 'It's better now that I can help her with homework, but at first I felt she just didn't need me any more.'

.... 'I'm finding it hard to see Stephen going to school. At first he was a baby and then a toddler. But now I have to realise that he's a boy and he's getting to be a big boy.'

.... 'When I saw all the other kids in the street going to the primary school up the road I just broke down.'

# At School Now

For at least eleven years and at a very formative stage of our development, we all attend some sort of school where we are exposed to a wide variety of messages and information, some of which we retain until the day we die, some of which we lose by breaktime the day we receive it. Whether we enjoy it or hate it, school is one of the influences in the life of the growing child. It represents children's first steps into the world outside their family, when for an extended period of time they are away from all they know best, with people and in surroundings which at first must seem very strange.

Children going to a special school may experience difficulties which other children do not come up against. The major issue is often that they are seen as 'different' because they attend a different school from most children in their own locality, and a school which may be described by the children they live close to in a variety of ways, most of them uncomplimentary. Because they may have to travel a long way to school their friends may live quite far away. It is vital therefore that from an early age, and certainly throughout their school years, disabled and handicapped children keep in contact with as many children in their own neighbourhood as possible, and as far as they are able. It is counterproductive to force them to do something against their will and could damage their confidence, but caring encouragement to play with other ordinary children helps everybody learn a bit more about what handicap really means in personal rather than abstract terms.

Special education has its roots away back in the latter half of the eighteenth century when Thomas Braidwood in the early 1760's set up the Academy for the Deaf and Dumb and Henry Dannett established the School of Instruction for the Indigent

Blind in Liverpool in 1791. While neither these nor many of the schools which followed rapidly can be said to have provided a very broad or thorough education as we might describe it today, they did establish the principles of *special needs*, and the recognition that these required different methods of fulfilment. It was however considerably later that provision was established for mentally handicapped children at Highgate in 1847, and for physically handicapped children at Marylebone in 1851.

Now it is the duty of all authorities to provide education for all children of school age with special educational needs in special schools, or in special classes or units attached to both primary and secondary schools.

## *Assessment*

Early identification of any form of handicap is crucial to the development of a child's potential, and much can be done to alleviate speech difficulties, poor muscle control and many other problems, by early intervention by an appropriate therapist. The local education authority co-ordinates an assessment by a doctor, a psychologist, and when a child is at school, a teacher, and parents are not only entitled but have a responsibility to be present at the examination as well as submitting in writing their own views as to the special eductional needs of their child. This assessment procedure may go ahead automatically after a child is identified by medical staff to have a disability. Parents who are concerned about their child's education can however contact the special education department in the local education authority office for more advice. In order to get the best attention for such an inquiry, parents should write first, then telephone perhaps two or three weeks later if they have not had a response.

## *Records of Needs (in Scotland)*
## *Statement of Special Educational Needs (in England)*

After the examination and assessment the authority then decides whether or not to open a *Record of Needs* or a *Statement of Special*

*Educational Needs* for the child, which details his or her special educational needs, and a copy of the draft of the record must be sent to parents for approval. The record is then kept up to date until the time a child leaves school or there ceases to be a need for the child to be recorded. Some parents may worry that by having a record or statement of needs their child may feel 'singled out' or in some way stigmatised, but this is a highly confidential document and can only benefit the child. It ensures regular assessment by a variety of professionals, and the provision of a statement of future needs drawn up for when the child is sixteen, some time between nine months and two years before. However where a parent does feel very strongly there are various means of appeal against it to the regional authority appeal committee, the sheriff (in Scotland) and ultimately the Secretary of State.

## *Named Person*

When the Record or Statement is drawn up, parents become entitled to nominate a *named person* to act as adviser, liaise with the authority and facilitate the provision of services to the recorded child. Parents select headteachers, ministers or their family doctor most often, although the choice is entirely theirs. In identifying a named person it is only wise to choose someone who knows his or her way round the various services available and who has experience in dealing with those in authority.

## *Special Education*

Today children are no longer categorised according to their handicap. The Education Act of 1981 in England and Education (Scotland) Act 1981 describe them as children 'with pronounced, specific or complex special educational needs' and emphasise the individual needs of different children. The special education system however works at a variety of levels, offering educational provision to those children with physical disability, with emotional or behavioural disorders, with mild mental handicap, and with severe or profound mental handicap. There are schools for children with hearing difficulties and with visual impairment, although for such children there is an increasing provision in mainstream schools, or in units attached to ordinary schools.

Where disabled children are in ordinary schools, education authorities provide peripatetic special education teachers to help their colleagues develop any special techniques which may be required in their teaching, and draw their attention to obvious aspects of their classroom or of their teaching style which might cause problems, like making sure any visual aids are large and clear enough for children with partial sight to see, not using coloured chalk with children who are colour-blind, and ensuring that a child with visual or hearing impairment sits at the front of the class and can see the teacher clearly. These visiting teachers are there to work individually with the disabled children when necessary, to give added support and help with any problems.

Increasing numbers of handicapped children are catered for in special classes attached to ordinary schools to promote integration. Such units have varying degrees of success and much of this success is dependent on the co-operation of the staff in the main school to accommodate the special needs of the pupils in the unit. There is a risk that the special pupils as a group become effectively isolated within the larger school population, but where staff show clear positive attitudes towards all the pupils then there is a spin-off throughout the school and benefits all round. The special pupils feel part of the large group and can begin to learn what life is like 'in the real world' without the protective wall that often keeps them separate, while the able-bodied pupils can through personal experience become more sensitive to the needs of disabled people, and realise that the barriers are not as great as many people think.

Despite the increasing attempts by local authorities to place children with special needs in mainstream education where possible, there is a continuing need for special schools, and it is unrealistic to suggest that such a need will ever cease to exist. Children with severe mental, physical or emotional problems need the smaller class environment — special schools have a maximum class size of fifteen — where the teacher can construct a programme specifically suited to individual needs. Most teachers in special education have been through an extra training designed to give them skills in different teaching techniques and to alert them to specific learning difficulties. That is not to say that the *aims* of special education are in any way different from ordinary education, but the methods and techniques used have to be designed for the various problems which disabled children have.

When your child goes to a special school, the headteacher should give you the school prospectus, which contains information about the school itself, and what the teachers do with the pupils. Throughout your child's time at school, the class teacher and headteacher should always be willing to talk over his or her progress, advise on extra physio- or speech therapy your child may need, and generally keep you informed. When you talk with the class teacher you may find that your child behaves differently at school from the way he does at home, but this is fairly common. For instance there was one boy who was an absolute gem in the school, very co-operative and willing, whose mother apologised profusely for his behaviour which was awful at home. She found it difficult to believe that anybody actually liked him! And the mother of one little girl, who changed her shoes herself twice a day as was necessary in the class, thought that she could not manage it herself at all, as it was always done for her at home by her grandmother. By talking with the class teacher, exchanging information and keeping in touch, you can help enormously, and at the same time learn quite a bit yourself!

# After Sixteen

For many young people sixteen marks a turning-point in their lives. Some decide to stay on at school while others make the transition from school pupil to potential member of the working population. Whatever your child decides at sixteen to do with the rest of his life will depend greatly on what his or her disability is. For many with sensory or physical difficulties the opportunities will be wider to a certain extent than for those youngsters with mental handicap. Some will opt for going on for higher education, and perhaps university. The majority however — just like 'normal' children — will leave school and begin to think about looking for a job with the help of the specialist careers officer based in the local education authority. As was said in the

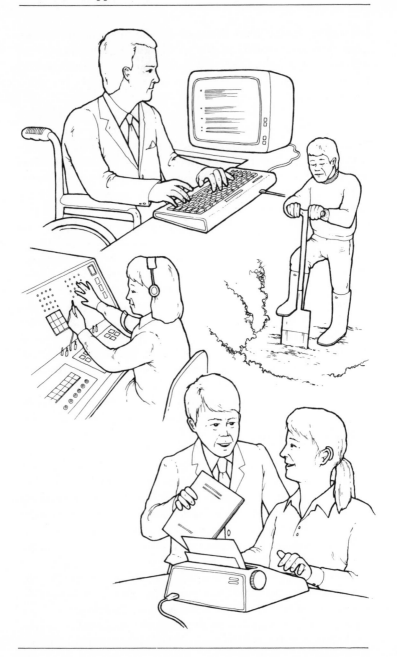

previous section, if your child is a recorded child a record of *future* needs will be provided by the assessment team, although the satisfaction or fulfilment of those needs may present some problems.

## *Housing*

Although many young people leave school at sixteen, most stay with one or both parents until they decide to set up house on their own or until they themselves find a partner. Many young disabled people will follow that pattern too and may not consider long-term accommodation a problem. Where there is a risk however that a young person may find it difficult, it is essential that parents consider the issue of long-term housing fairly early on for several reasons. Parents may find that the assessment procedures prior to application are lengthy and complicated. Having gone through those, they may find that waiting lists can be up to two or three years long. Many residential facilities can be very choosy about their residents because of the shortage of suitable accommodation. They may specify that prospective residents have certain skills in dressing and toileting or they may have to be ambulant. Many parents shy off making a decision about where their child will stay in future because they feel a loving responsibility to provide a home for each of their children for as long as these children need one. It has to be said too that many parents recognise — even if they do not admit it — that they would be very lonely or aimless if they did not have somebody to look after and cook and keep house for. But everybody has to grow old, and in so doing may not have quite as much 'get up and go' as previously. No matter how willing the spirit, the flesh becomes older and generally weaker. As an older parent you too are entitled to your own independence and the opportunity to enjoy a little more freedom than is ever available when children are little.

Most parents with handicapped children worry about who will make sure that their child is all right after they themselves are no longer there or able to do so. By keeping their child at home parents may in fact be adding to the problem.

Their youngster will almost certainly *not* develop as much

independence by staying at home as by experiencing life away from a caring parent. When a natural and inevitable break comes through the death of that parent the disabled adult may have to cope not only with the loss of his mother or father, but also with a move into residential accommodation, and be emotionally less equipped to deal with such a situation which is in itself a major life event.

Your social worker or, after sixteen, your young person's social worker should be able to help by suggesting the various options available through local statutory services. Other organisations which can help include:

Ark Housing Association Ltd
8 Balcarres Street
Edinburgh 10 (031-447 9027)

Central Council for the Disabled
34 Eccleston Square
London (01-821 1871)

Disabled Living Foundation
346 Kensington High Street
London (01-602 2491)

John Grooms Housing Association
10 Gloucester Drive
Finsbury Park
London (01-802 7272)

Key Housing Association
13 Elmbank Street
Glasgow (041-226 4868)

Margaret Blackwood Housing Association
32 Inglis Green Road
Edinburgh (031-443 5634)

MENCAP Homes Foundation
Royal Society for Mentally Handicapped Children
and Adults
123 Golden Lane
London EC1Y 0RT (01-253 9433)

Scottish Federation of Housing Associations
42 York Place
Edinburgh (031-556 1435)

There are lots more organisations concerned with residential facilities, but many of these cater only for those living in their own locality. Their addresses should be available from your social work or social services department.

# Further education

For youngsters with all different kinds of handicap who decide to leave school at sixteen there are many opportunities to continue learning at further education colleges, the majority of which run courses designed for those who are visually or hearing impaired, and for slow learners. However, local education authorities are required to provide school education up to the age of nineteen for all children with learning difficulties. While staying on at school helps some children develop their potential, it can to a certain extent prevent their maturing as they would in a more adult environment, so both pros and cons have to be considered in the best interest of the child. For those slow learners who are placed in adult training centres, or social education centres in England and Wales, education forms a very large part of the day-to-day programme with the emphasis on social education and 'education for life', for example social and communication skills and training for independence.

Those children with sensory or physical handicap who opt for higher education will probably have developed their own best methods of study by the time they take this decision. In their last year at school and throughout their time at college they should join the local branch of the National Union of Students. By increasing the numbers of disabled students in the NUS, greater

27

pressure can be put on the powers that be to provide specialist facilities such as ramps and support bars where necessary. The Central Bureau for Educational Visits and Exchanges, Seymour Mews House, 26-37 Seymour Mews, London (01-486 5101), and the National Bureau for Handicapped Students, 40 Brunswick Square, London (01-278 3459) are two useful addresses to contact for information about exchange visits, courses and educational facilities.

Everybody benefits from continuing to learn and expand interests. For disabled young people, whether severely mentally handicapped or physically or sensorily impaired, education is vital for their healthy and complete development.

# Employment

In these days of high unemployment, world recession and mass redundancies, the issue of employment is a political and social hot potato.

With increasing automation, jobs previously done by people with mild mental handicap are now completed by machines tailor-made for the job. Many mentally impaired young people however go into adult training centres, where as well as having a high educational component, activities consist of employment in a variety of industrial tasks. Sheltered workshops, too, provide industrial training for mentally and physically handicapped people. These are administered by the local social work or social services department who can be contacted for more information.

Employers with a staff of over 20 are required to employ a quota of 3% of disabled people, and in each area a *Disablement Resettlement Officer* is there to advise disabled people on training, help them obtain suitable work, and identify aids where necessary.

For those unable to work in open employment, many voluntary organisations run sheltered workshops, while Remploy, set up in the forties, has factories throughout the country for disabled workers. Their head office is Remploy House, 415 Edgware Road, Cricklewood, London (01-452 8020).

# *Leisure*

The employment prospects for disabled people are not as good as they might be. Social attitudes prevail against their employment and the size of the work pool of able-bodied people, along with practical problems such as access, discriminate heavily against disabled people being offered jobs in many walks of life. For many severely handicapped people, employment is out of the question because of their disabilities.

With the prospect of so much free time ahead, long before children leave school they should be encouraged to structure their leisure time so that it is used productively and positively. That is not to say that play should turn into hard work, but with the choice of channels now on television, it may be too easy to opt for sitting in front of the box without really thinking about what is on. Disabled children may stay in and watch television even more than the average twenty-three hours per week, at times like Saturday afternoon and early Sunday evening when other children are doing other things.

They may sometimes be watching television passively, to mark time and fill in the hours when they are not at school. There is much debate about the effects of television and video — especially 'video nasties' — on children and adolescents today and very little in the way of conclusive evidence in any one direction. But it stands to reason that a child who is sacrificing time to watch programmes which he may not understand, or which he does not remember only minutes after they are finished, is not employed in an activity which is either relaxing, educational or sociable.

There are many organisations which run local clubs for young handicapped people to meet and chat with each other and enjoy a variety of activities. These are most often run for slow learners or mentally disabled people by the local mental handicap association, while Physically Handicapped and Able Bodied (PHAB) based at 42 Devonshire Street, London (01-637 7475), has over three hundred branches throughout the United Kingdom, and organises clubs, residential courses and informal get-togethers. The Sports Council, 70 Brompton Road, London (01-589 3411) and Scottish Sports Council, 1 St Colme Street,

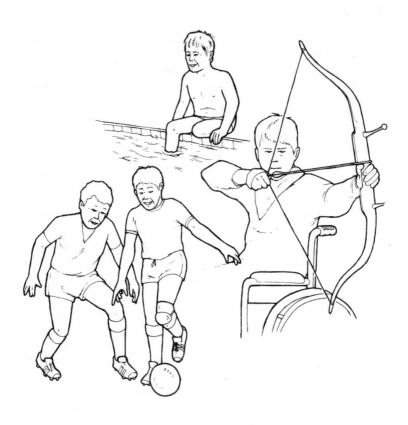

Edinburgh (031-225 8411) provide advice and information on opportunities at both local and national level for children and adults with all different kinds of handicap. Several others are listed later on page   . In many areas too there are officers who have responsibility for the leisure and recreation services for handicapped children and adults, and they organise classes, courses and events. Many of those involved with sport and disability say that the only limitations which disabled children and adults have are those inflicted on them by the difficulties of the environment, the normal limitations of being human. After all, 'normal' people cannot do everything either.

# Independence

For many children with disability, future independence is something they take for granted, given that they have acquired the skills to cope with and overcome their individual difficulties. For many others with more severe physical or mental disabilities life will always hold some degree of dependence on other people. The complement to that is that these children and young people will have a degree — more or less — of independence also. As children grow into adults, it is in the nature of things that they want to have an increasing say in many aspects of their day-to-day living. Just because parents have to do almost as much for them as teenagers as when they were young children does not alter this fact. Indeed for the young person the degree of independence may be highlighted, and the determination to hold on to whatever independence he does have may be increased. This time may be difficult for you to rationalise all the conflicting feelings of wanting your child to be as independent a person as possible while at the same time recognising the extent of his need for you to be around.

All parents have problems with teenagers and it is wise not to lose sight of this perhaps trite, but nonetheless true, social fact. No matter how severely handicapped, young people should be encouraged to take part in discussions relating to any decisions taken which will affect them. Even something as simple as asking them what they want to eat instead of deciding for them can go a long way to build confidence in someone for whom other decisions would be too complex.

They should also be encouraged to have their own friends outside the family. One parent said of Mary, her severely mentally handicapped daughter 'She goes out more than I do.' By inviting other young people into your home, and recognising the need to have friends of a similar age, you are allowing your youngster the freedom to be a person in his or her own right.

# Money matters

Various things — having a circle of friends, being asked to contribute an opinion to a decision, however trivial — help a handicapped youngster to build up his self-esteem. It is also vital that he feels he has an independent income, however small. Whatever their handicap, all disabled young people who are unable to work are entitled to a non-contributory invalidity pension and may be entitled in addition to supplementary benefit and single payments for clothing, laundry and several other things. Even where a person is working in sheltered employment, depending on his wage he may still be entitled to supplementary benefit and all that brings with it, including free dental treatment, prescriptions and glasses. Youngsters who are disabled and have to attend hospital may claim their transport costs by asking for a transport claim form from the hospital administrative staff who will forward it to the proper authorities.

When a young person is mentally handicapped he may at best be able to deal with his money in only a very concrete way. In other words he may be able to count and spend the money he has in his pocket but the concept of making money last for a few days, or saving money, may be something he cannot understand. Some people are so severely handicapped that they do not understand money at all.

Banks are able to open accounts for people and then appoint a Curator Bonis who will administer and look after the account. You as a parent will want to make as much provision as possible for a youngster who will need care after your death. It is wise to consult a lawyer on this since it is not simply a case of leaving money set aside. It is wise too to have a will so that there is no risk of legal wrangling and delay at a time when the people who are left least need extra pressure.

Again relating only to mentally handicapped people, voting rights, and the decision whether your eighteen-year-old should have, and would understand, a vote is entirely at your discretion or, if he or she is in long-term care, at the discretion of the authority in the residential facility.

Independence is something which means different things to different people. Nobody has total control over his or her life, and many people have very little indeed. It is crucial for our feelings of self-esteem and value as a person that we exert as much control as we can cope with — too much independence can be as dangerous or frightening as too little is frustrating and destructive. By encouraging your youngster to develop skills of independence and decision-making within his own capabilities, you are offering him one of the greatest opportunities possible — to be a person.

# Value Judgement

'There's nowt as funny as folk' goes the old adage, and there is a lot of truth in it. Some people on the surface may seem calm and confident, and yet their insides may be churning, while others may appear to be aggressive and over-confident but in fact be overcompensating for their own shyness. Many people however do have confidence in themselves and a realistic picture or image of themselves which helps them project their own personality and value themselves as people. Such confidence and self-esteem grow and develop over years, and initially are largely dependent on how parents, relatives and people in general treat an individual from a very early age. So a baby who is welcomed and valued has a greater start in life than a child who may not be wanted by either one or both of the parents. Children are very quick to pick up feelings, indeed they rely on them to communicate with the people around them before they can speak, and for a long time after. Children who are sensorily disabled however may miss many of the non-verbal cues by which people show their feelings; they may not see people smiling, or see warmth in their parents' eyes, they may not hear warmth and love in people's voices. Children who are mentally impaired may not understand as quickly or completely as other children, while children who are physically disabled may feel that they are not the same as their able-bodied counterparts. Whatever your child's handicap, it is important that he or she learns from you that you want to have him with you and that he is important to you. He may need an extra input of cuddles, tickles and kisses throughout his formative years, but who would complain about that?

As children grow and develop, go to school and begin to take up the threads of adult life, they all come in contact with people who are nice to them, people who are nasty to them, people who shout at them and people who will give them large doses of 'tender loving care'. A person's self-image and self-esteem is formed and reformed with each contact so that if a child is constantly told that he is a good or friendly child, he 'learns' that he is such, and acts in that manner. Unfortunately disabled children may come in contact with people who think they are strange or different, and just as a child will learn from people around him that he is friendly, he may learn that he is 'different' or 'ugly' and begin to believe it.

To combat this very real risk parents, carers and brothers and sisters can make sure that a child, whatever his disability, takes part in as many family activities as possible, such as taking a walk, fetching a message, going out for a meal, even though the practicalities of it may be a little more difficult. It may be quicker just to nip down to the shops yourself, or it may be easier to send the rest of the family off to play football while you stay at home and babysit your disabled child, but.... By getting him accustomed to curious or rude stares or inconsiderate and impertinent comments, you will help him cope more adequately in future.

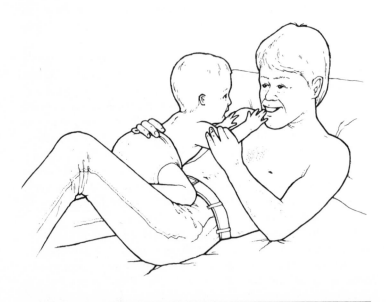

But it does not stop there. Human beings are by nature fairly gregarious and need social contact to maintain their wellbeing. Indeed one of the first signs of emotional distress in a person is when he becomes withdrawn and finds it difficult to get on with other people. When a child is disabled in some way he may not be able to make the first move towards other children. He may not instinctively practise the social steps which children use to make contact with each other. The less he meets and plays with other children the more he will 'learn' that he is a loner or that he is socially more isolated than other children.

Children — of all ages — need to have contact with people of their own age or interests outside their immediate family and it is up to you as a parent to encourage your disabled child out into the world. There he will undoubtedly receive some knocks, but there he will also build up social acumen and confidence which will go towards his feeling of being a valued and contributing member of his society. It may also help him develop a thicker social skin which will protect him when you are not around to do so.

# 3. Family Matters

## A Handicapped Child in the Family

'Family' is a word that means a lot of things to a lot of different people — a one- or two-parent family, a family setting in a residential home, a foster family or short-term care scheme.

Whatever your family situation, life at home can be difficult at the best of times trying to reconcile increased financial and social demands from members of the family with what can appear to be static, if not dwindling, resources. For parents who have a child with some kind of disabling condition, the pressures may be of a different kind, although perhaps no more or less than for those with 'normal' children. It has to be said that the joys and delights can also be as great even if measured by a different yardstick.

One father whose third child, his only daughter, was a Down's baby said 'Charlotte has brought such joy into the family — she's a delight.' Mothers have said…. 'It can be difficult, but I wouldn't change him'…. 'You may wish that things had been different, but you learn to accept things as they are.'

### *Going out*

Parents with a handicapped child often find that facing the family is difficult, but at least you can be fairly sure in the majority of cases that whatever their initial reactions have been there is care and concern for your welfare and that of your child from relatives and close friends. Their motives in trying to deal with the situation will be of the best even if at times they appear to be misplaced.

Facing the general public may be quite a different matter, however. When you go out, people may stare excessively, or avoid you if your child is in a wheelchair or has identifiable features, such as with Down's Syndrome. Understandably, many parents find this difficult. One mother smilingly reports that when she takes her now fifteen-year-old son out in his chair old ladies will often come up and spontaneously press some money into her hand with concerned expressions of sympathy but a notable lack of understanding. One father more acidly recalls picking his twenty-two-year-old mentally impaired daughter up from a church social event where she had been ignored for most of the evening. He says 'I wanted to go up to people and grab them by the lapels and say "Look, she's a person too".'

## Your own attitudes

The reactions of other people, from close relatives to passers-by, depend largely on you and the way you handle each situation as it arises. Many parents have never had any experience of disability until they have their special child, and like many people who form the general public, have vague or unclear attitudes to disability and what it implies. It is vital therefore to know your own feelings about disabled children and adults, so that what comes across to other people is positive, and not a double or conflicting message. One useful way to go about sorting out your own attitudes is to read what other parents have written about their experiences and to investigate what many disabled people have either said or written about their personal disability and how it has affected their lives. Some of these are to be found on pages 44-51.

Many people find it more valuable to talk their feelings out with a partner, with a close friend or with a sympathetic professional, perhaps a doctor, home visiting teacher or health visitor. Parents' groups are very valuable for many people who find that by exchanging opinions, ideas and feelings with others who have experienced similar situations, they can more easily put their own child into perspective.

## Time to spare

The birth of a new baby and the rearing of a growing child takes a lot of time and effort, patience and emotion. Whether your child is born with a difficulty or whether he or she becomes disabled through illness or accident, you are liable to have spent some time with medical staff either caring for you, or your child. No matter how caring staff are, it can be fairly stressful, and it is important that you settle down to *your own way of life* as soon as possible.

It may sound selfish, but for your own sake, you must take time to relax and enjoy your own pursuits and interests. Even by putting your feet up for ten minutes by yourself, you will be 'recharging your battery' and building up reserves of energy. After a while you may be able to leave your baby with a sitter with experience of disabled children. Your social work or social services department or parents' group may be able to help suggest sources such as a local sitting service or the Crossroads Attendance Scheme. The Attendance Allowance which you will receive will help towards charges.

As a parent, you may be the major carer of the baby, and it is crucial that you maintain your health and wellbeing, so that you know your child will always be in good hands. There is risk however that as *major* carer, you may fall into the role of *sole* carer — with no time to spare for yourself. It is just as important for your child that he learns to stay for a short time with other people, secure in the knowledge that you will be back. Many social work or social service departments operate 'Share the Care' schemes which offer short-term, even a half or one day relief care, to families in which there is a handicapped child. You may feel that by joining an evening class in, say, car maintenance, or self-defence, you are meeting new people and building up a new interest or skill. You may however decide that your free time, however short, is best spent chatting with a friend over a drink, or going to the cinema.

All parents of disabled children have tremendous strains upon them in bringing up their children. As a single parent you may have nobody really close to share your feelings with, although this may also be true of many marriages. Both mothers and fathers have their own personal reactions as well as those of their partner to cope with. Many marriages break up under the strain of raising a disabled child, while many couples feel that their relationship was strengthened in the face of trouble. It is more often the case that the mother has most to do with the baby, and there may be a risk that her partner may feel redundant. A woman may find that she has not as much time as in the past to spend with her partner to do things they enjoyed together. On the practical side, everyday tasks may take up so much time and effort that many little extras go by the board.

## *What makes families tick — Talk*

As far as you are able you should ensure that family life goes on as you want it to, without anyone having to sacrifice because there is a handicapped family member. Family life should not revolve around your disabled child but should offer each family member a place to be secure, to be happy or miserable, to be his or her own self.

As a parent you are there to be a shoulder to cry on, to support and to enjoy all members of your family. As a partner you are there to share a relationship in which you have a fifty-per-cent stake. By bottling things up, you may only be building up a head of steam which will blow, inevitably at the wrong moment. Every member of the family should have a share in

responsibilities of all kinds, from doing the dishes to sorting out the family finances. Talking about any pressures you may be under, or decisions which you have to make, admitting your feelings honestly, even only to yourself, helps you to take the best from and contribute the most to the life-style of your family whether it consists of only two or of twenty people.

# Brothers and Sisters

One decision which parents who have a handicapped baby must face is whether to have more children. Where the handicapped child is an only child this issue is even more gruelling. Parents may not want to 'burden' younger children with a handicapped elder brother or sister. They may worry that they are having other children to compensate for their disabled child. They will most certainly be afraid that their next child will be handicapped too. Much of the decision will depend on the nature of the child's handicap and may indeed be influenced by religious or cultural beliefs. Problems during pregnancy or birth trauma are human accidents which antenatal care services and obstetric medical staff are working to alleviate. Screening tests during pregnancy can detect spina bifida and Down's Syndrome, and parents then can decide to terminate the pregnancy. Genetic counselling is available in most areas through the family doctor. Couples who have a family history of muscular dystrophy or Friedreich's Ataxia should certainly consult these services if they are contemplating a pregnancy.

There is no right or wrong decision for all families. 'Normal' children can help and support their parents and their handicapped brother or sister, while other parents feel glad that they are able to devote all their time and energies to their only, handicapped, child.

The majority of families with a handicapped child have other children who are either older or younger, or both. It is interesting to note that despite the huge quantity of research into sibling relationships in families without handicapped children, there is little research into the effects of a handicapped child on brothers and sisters.

The little that has been done tends to suggest that older sisters have much more to do with the handicapped youngster than do brothers, and that much of the perception of the handicapped child's difficulties and his or her role in the family is dependent on the way the parents have dealt with the issue of handicap and how they have passed on information to the other children.

Children are very quick to pick up that all is not well and can worry that they have been instrumental in causing situations which in fact they have nothing to do with. It is only fair and just that they are given clear factual information as soon as possible in a way that they can best understand. By involving them right from the very beginning you are encouraging a healthy attitude towards your handicapped child's difficulties instead of turning them into something mysterious or something to be ashamed of.

As the children grow older they will face questions from their friends, and if they are to handle these competently they must have a clear understanding themselves of the situation, especially where there is the possibility of embarrassment about aids such as catheters or problems with communication. You may find that they ask you why you have had a handicapped baby or why you did not have an ordinary baby. Children can be unwittingly cruel in their search for knowledge and understanding.

Many parents are surprised when they realise just how much their other children are concerned or worried about their handicapped brother or sister. Many youngsters express their worries when the disabled child goes to school since in many cases it will be a special school and therefore different from the one they went to themselves.

Many worry too about what will happen in the future when parents are no longer there to take responsibility for their disabled brother or sister. This of course depends greatly on the nature and severity of the disability but for children with severe disabilities who will live only semi-independently as adults it is of vital importance that parents consider provision for their long-term care, and that they talk this over with any other children in the family, as a family with mutual concern and responsibility for each other's welfare.

By encouraging — but not forcing — your other children to include your handicapped child as much as possible in their games, by encouraging them to bring friends home and by spreading the feeling of responsibility, *not for your disabled child alone* but for each other, you are building on the foundations of a healthy family life.

Many older parents recall not very happily that they tended to spend more time with their handicapped child than with their other children. While as an everyday time commitment this may be necessary in practical terms it is unjust not only to your other children but also to yourself and your disabled child. Many families consider a holiday without their disabled child as disloyal and a betrayal of their care. The possibility should not be too quickly discounted, however, as it has benefits for all family members to have a change of scene, and short-term holiday relief can help introduce a young disabled child to the situation of being away from mummy and daddy without its being a permanent break. The local social work or social services department should be able to organise such holiday care, but the special education department may also be able to help.

# Sharing out the Cake

Running a home and raising a family these days is an increasingly expensive business, even just providing the basic necessities, never mind the many little extras which can make life that much better. When you have a child with some kind of disability you may find that you need to buy special clothing or special equipment specifically suited to his needs. Much of this is available through your social work, social services or health departments, and you should ask your doctor, health visitor or social worker about equipment or aids which you can claim.

## *Benefits and allowances*

There are two allowances to which you may be entitled over and above the Child Benefit Allowance which all parents receive.

The Attendance Allowance is payable from when a baby is very young throughout a disabled person's life and can be claimed at two levels — on a twenty-four-hour basis when a child or adult requires someone to be there all the time, or on a twelve-hour basis during the day or night. The Attendance Allowance may be used to pay sitters so that parents or permanent carers can have some time to follow their own interests and pursuits outside the home.

The Mobility Allowance is payable, after a medical examination, to people who cannot walk or have excessive difficulty with mobility. This allowance can be used to purchase a car where necessary through the organisation Motability whose address is on page 75. Where a child has mobility problems but has access to a car, either that of parents, friends or relatives, he or she is entitled to what is known as the 'Orange Badge', the little sticker with the familiar disability sign which can be attached to the car window so that the car can stop in places where vehicles are not normally permitted.

These allowances are not charitable hand-outs — you and other members of your family have contributed through taxation of all sorts. They are your right as a member of a society which recognises that many forms of disability bring added expense and which, as a caring society, recognises the responsibility to provide support where needed.

## Housing

As a baby your child can be carried or pushed around like any other baby. As he grows older however, you should encourage him to explore his environment as much as possible. You may find that steps or doorways in your house which you had never really given much thought to, suddenly become a problem, especially if your child has mobility problems. If your house has two storeys the likelihood is that the bathroom is on the top storey up a flight of stairs which is not negotiable by even the smallest and most manoeuvrable of wheelchairs.

Grants are available through social work and social services departments for renovations to houses where necessary for the installation of a downstairs bathroom, for support bars, ramps or for any other changes which your house may need to allow your child to move as freely as possible round his home with the maximum convenience.

# Personal Experience

Over the years of caring for and raising a handicapped child, parents will come in contact with many professional people and many workers who will help, advise and offer information. Many professionals are very knowledgeable about special care, and are invaluable supports to parents. Many professionals however do not have the *personal* experience of having a handicapped child, so parents' groups can be useful settings where people can talk about how they *feel*, in the comforting knowledge that the rest of the group will appreciate their feelings because they have been down that road themselves.

Here are two parents' experiences.

When my son, my second child, was born, my husband and I were very pleased with ourselves. We already had a five-year-old daughter and we felt we had achieved the perfect nuclear family. He was born with little difficulty at about 8.30am on a sunny summer Sunday in June and he weighed 8lbs 10ozs. Although we were overjoyed, we wondered how our daughter would feel because she wanted a baby sister, so that she could be the same as her best friend. The other trivial detail that flitted through my head was that my beautiful little son looked a very odd pale, bluish-grey colour. When I mentioned this to the midwife she replied, 'Have you ever seen a new-born baby who *isn't* a funny colour?' Well, as a matter of fact, I hadn't. My daughter was born slightly jaundiced and at birth she wore what looked like a gorgeous suntan. So I really *had* never seen a new baby who wasn't a funny colour. Much later, when our world fell to pieces around us, it occurred to me, though, that the midwife must have seen babies who *were* a perfectly acceptable colour. After all, I had been involved in only two births. She had been in attendance at a great many.

I was anxious to breast-feed my son, since I had fed my daughter for 8½ months until she had four teeth and the whole process ceased to be quite as pleasurable as once it had been. My son would not fix (it was really 'could not', although we did not know about that at that stage). He was nearly always asleep, but when he was awake he cried with a strange breathy mewing cry. None of these details gave me cause for concern at that time. I rationalised to myself that boys were probably completely different from girls and if I at any time voiced my thoughts to the nursing staff they reinforced my rationalisation. They said things like, 'He's a big baby and won't need to be fed so often' or 'He's asleep in the nursery; it would be a shame to wake him up', and their reassuring answers made me feel that perhaps I was being just another fussy mother.

However, on the third day after he was born, I waited and waited for him to be brought to me. I knew that my best friend and my mother were both coming to see me and I was looking forward to showing off my fine son. Visiting time came and went without the appearance of the baby, in spite of requests, questions and pleas to the nursing staff to bring him whether he was asleep or awake.

Eventually I was told that Dr. B. would be coming to talk to me about my baby, but that in the meantime there was nothing at all to worry about. In the evening, before my husband came to see me, Dr. B. arrived. He sat down in a chair near me and talked. *How* he talked! I made very little sense of what he said and he left no gaps in the conversation for me to fill. All that I could gather was that my son was in the Special Care Unit and that they were keeping an eye on him there. My first thought was for my husband. I didn't want him to be worried and asked the doctor what I should tell him when he arrived at visiting time. I was immediately put at ease when Dr. B. assured me that he would himself tell my husband, and that I could see my baby any time I wanted to. I was asked to tell my husband to go to see Dr. B. after the visiting time was over.

I still find it very painful to recall the next few days and weeks of that hot summer. My husband was told many harsh clinical facts about our son which he was told he could divulge to me or not as he saw fit. Of course, he told me what he thought he had heard and we tried to piece together the information each had been given. None of it made very much sense to us. All we could grasp was that our son was very ill but neither of us knew what was the matter with him.

The first major blow fell when I realised that my son, so far from being breast-fed, needed to be fed via a tube up his nose.

The next crunch came when we were told that he was having 'twitches'. We eventually realised that these twitches were, in fact, epileptic seizures.

It was hinted that he was having breathing difficulties, and it was then that we saw for ourselves the oxygen next to his little cot. Eventually we were told that Professor X. would like to talk to us. In my mind I can still see him, grim-faced and bespectacled with thick, hairy eye-brows and two little 'horns' of hair on either side of his head — Mephistopheles himself! His manner was brusque and to the point. He told us that, in the unlikely event of our son surviving the week-end, he could not predict what he would be like. He might be epileptic; he might be mentally handicapped; he might be physically handicapped; he was very likely to be all three. We were plunged into the depths of hell with the Devil himself.

The next time-span is very confused in my mind. I remember counting steps, counting lamp-posts, avoiding cracks in the pavement. If the counting added up to an odd number, or worst of all, thirteen, I felt very anxious and upset. I felt very distressed if I saw a proud new mother pushing a pram, in a shop or anywhere at all. If I try to analyse that feeling, I think I was upset because no-one could tell when they saw me that I had a new baby, too.

My husband would suddenly find himself in the car at some strange destination with no remembrance of having driven there nor any idea of why he was there.

My parents and my mother-in-law were distressed and unhappy for us. They were bewildered, as we were, but did what they could to help. They visited very frequently and were there when we needed to talk of the baby or when we needed to talk of other things.

Some friends and neighbours would cross the street if they saw us coming. At the time I was very hurt by this. I wanted to talk about my son, even to weep about him, and felt deserted and alone when someone 'passed by on the other side'.

The friends and neighbours who did NOT pass by made up a hundredfold for those who did. One neighbour endeared herself to us forever by telephoning in case I was lonely or alone, by leaving little notes with messages like 'Thinking of you' written on them. After a particularly harrowing visit to the hospital, we returned home to find red roses on our doorstep. The tears shed on seeing them were quite different from the ones shed on the way home.

Days passed; weeks passed, and our frail little blossom did not wither and die. If he did not exactly bloom and flourish, at least he still clung on to the branch. I longed to have him at home where he could take his place in the family, even for a little while, but the medical staff at the hospital felt that he needed more constant care than could be provided at home. However, it seemed to me to be more sensible for one person to be caring for him all the time than an ever-changing team of nursing staff, however competent. So, finding a determination within myself that I had not been aware of before, I told the consultant in charge that I would be taking my son home. To say that he looked startled would be no less than the truth. However, I was given every help and guidance possible and was also assured that, if at any time the going became too tough, Alasdair would be re-admitted to hospital with but a moment's notice.

I still marvel that we survived the next period of time as a family. Of course, I had not fully appreciated how difficult life would be with Alasdair at home. He was unable to suck strongly enough to feed himself, so milk had to be given him using a pumping technique which only I could do. He was fed 3 hourly right round the clock which meant that I was never able to sleep for any more than 2 hours at a time since it took almost an hour to push about 1 ½ ozs of milk into him. But, worst of all, with terrible relentless regularity, ten minutes after he was fed, he would vomit what looked like a gallon of milk all over the place. He generally managed to retain the feed given in the wee small hours, so I dared not sleep through that time.

I am not quite sure what or how the rest of us managed to eat. My husband worked away quietly, making up feeds, doing the shopping, helping with washing (*and* ironing!), taking our daughter to and from school and trying to do a full day's work as an architect as well. I could never at any time say that, in our marriage, we have 'never had a cross word', but in the care and management of Alasdair it has definitely been team work.

The third member of that team has always been our daughter. In lighter moments — and there have been an amazing number of them — I have always said that, if you must have a handicapped child in your family, make sure you have a daughter five years before. We quite deliberately treated her like a third parent for Alasdair as soon as he came home, making her feel, we hoped, that she was indispensable to us and to her brother. She was allowed to pick him up if she wanted to, and we have a very amusing photograph of a brightly smiling five-year-old lovingly hugging a rather saggy baby, much in the same way that children cuddle cats.

Every evening my husband and daughter played hilarious bathtime games while I gave Alasdair yet another ill-received feed. Later on, my husband would care for the baby while Elizabeth and I closed the door of her bedroom firmly behind us and enjoyed 'Winnie-the-Pooh', 'Peter Rabbit', 'The Cat in the Hat', and all the children's literature that we strongly believed to be her heritage — as it was her right to have our time for herself.

Throughout the years, she has matured early and has always been unafraid to take decisions for herself. She also has an awareness of the needs of others and has never shirked hard work. She has been my best friend for some time now and I value her help and advice. All this does not mean that we always see eye-to-eye. Her father would be able to groan, hold his head and bear witness to the fact that we do not.

Had our son not survived, we had made a firm decision to have at least one other child as soon as possible. However, he did and needed so much looking after and attention, that we made up our minds that to have another child would be fair to no-one.

The problems of bringing up Alasdair have changed as he has grown. Amazingly, he is now sixteen and a force to be reckoned with! He is still unable to walk, dress or feed himself. He is also doubly incontinent. But — he can recognise (and enjoy) a flute, a violin, a piano, a trumpet. He knows a sparrow, a sea-gull, a pigeon, a blackbird and a robin. He has a 'best friend' and, best of all he chatters cheerfully all day long.

We try, as we have always done, to take each day as it comes, but we are naturally anxious about what the future holds. How long will he be able to stay at school, where he is so happy? How long will he continue in the reasonably good health he enjoys at the moment? What will happen if he survives us? How will we cope if he does not? I have no answers — only doubts and fears, and these I seldom allow out for an airing.

---

Joe was born three weeks late, covered in little white spots and with multiple congenital abnormalities — which included a cleft palate, club foot, displaced hips and severe breathing difficulties. The white spots went, the cleft palate and the club foot were repaired, but the breathing difficulties were caused by a malformation of the spine, and remain. His mind is bright and merry.

I was told that he was 'not very well' by a doctor I'd never seen before, and as much of the truth as he knew it by my husband — who was very shaken and tired. He had been with me through most of my long three-day labour. We were both upset that I had to have a caesarean and I was frustrated and angry at not having the baby by the natural methods I'd practised, so I probably didn't quite take in the news. When it did sink in several hours later I began to hope that I didn't have to see him if he wasn't going to survive. In fact I did not see him for 24 hours and then it was such a surprise. He did not look like my husband, as I had somehow expected, but like a miniature of my father. I think I was pleased but the memory is one of surprise. My mother coped much better with the news that her first grandchild was not in perfect health than did my father. He wept, quietly but sadly — somehow the baby looking like him made it worse. I remember apologising to everyone — 'Sorry', I said. 'He really isn't as well as he should be' — as though I'd made some ghastly mistake. My husband's parents were always rather reserved and seemed to retreat together even more than before.

Telling friends and relatives was my husband's task — I was in hospital for a while and when he came to visit me he was quite grey in the face. I tried to help by writing letters but gave up after just a few because I couldn't cope with putting it down in black and white.

But Joe survived. He was unable to suck because of the cleft palate so I was not able to breast-feed him and he was kept in hospital for months before we could take him home. The whole family and friends rallied round to make it possible for us to visit and visit and visit this small being. I'll always be grateful to the ward sister at the hospital who made sure we understood the importance of making a good relationship with our son from the very start. We helped change him, bath him and feed him — by tube, in splints, in an oxygen tent. That tent and others like it were to become part of our lives for years to come. At that time neither my husband nor I could drive so my father drove us to the hospital before going to work and my husband went to his work after the first feed. My brother collected me from the hospital at lunch-time, took me home to do my housework, and I made my way back for the evening feed when my husband joined me after his day at the college where he was teaching. Friends often came and took us home by car. The staff were young and energetic and urged us on with encouragement and hope. One particular young doctor who was lame was a constant source of energy and example. We were too busy to know how tired we were. We simply took each day as it came, and he survived.

Joe was six months old when he came home. Having a new baby — well, almost new baby — at home was quite different from the security of the hospital ward. We were lucky again in our GP, who became our counsellor and friend and teller of faintly blue jokes in the wee small hours as we waited together while Joe came through yet another convulsion. Friends were enthusiastic to visit but even with the best of intentions what could they say about a very, very thin child, with both legs in splints, being sick after every meal? They tried though, and one dear friend who brought a pale yellow sleeping suit as a gift said 'He'll look just like an unripe banana in this', and he did!

After the first year he seemed to grow out of the convulsions and the sickness, but the chest infections were many and often. The local children's hospital became our second home and we made many friends — the young registrar who climbed the drainpipe to Joe's window with fish and chips for him after a bad day, Matron taking part in a snowball fight in the cubicle where Joe was on a respirator during a nasty bout of bronchitis, and the consultant too, who challenged Joe to a wheelchair slalom down the ward, shortly after he became wheelchair bound. This happened after an operation to relieve pressure on the spinal column. He was in hospital for two years that time and that was when he lost his voice too. Joe was 12 years old and I was devastated. But he continued to communicate with the nurses in a very faint whisper, with lots of hand movements and using his eyes a lot. There was a great deal of hilarity — and he managed to be understood. I was humbled, if he could take this further blow then so could I, but it was hard. Our friends and relatives found this new handicap really quite hard to cope with and some of them, particularly the older ones, still have some difficulty understanding everything he says. He can make two very clear sounds, a piercing whistle and a very splashy raspberry. The whistle generally means approval and the other sound — quite the reverse.

About this time we became aware that Joe was growing up and although small in stature he was almost 14 years old and male. The nurses who were caring for him were 17 and 18 years old and female. I wondered how he saw them, but try as I might, my son would not communicate his thoughts about his attractive nurses to me. All I got from him when I said something like 'She's nice, isn't she?' was a nod or a raspberry! He seemed to get on well with them though and when he went to his present day centre, I noted that he chose an attractive young O.T. to confide in.

How much does any mother know of her son's sexual awareness? I'm not sure I know much about Joe's. I know he likes women, and he writes regularly to a lass he met at a sports meeting (he wins slalom races now). If I ask him about her he is polite but I can sense that raspberry around. It was much in evidence when I suggested he might go to the series of talks on sex that were being offered at his day centre. He just looked at me, blew his raspberry and wheeled swiftly off to do something more interesting like archery or bowls. Is this because he is physically handicapped? Or is it a normal reaction from a young man who thinks Mum is trying to organise him.

Joe is 24 now and works in a sheltered workshop for young physically handicapped. However this did not happen easily and there was a time, when he was 16 and 17, when we wondered if we were all to be condemned to boredom, housebound forever.

There are no regrets about having Joe. The work has been hard and still continues but we have also shared pleasure and pride in his achievements — many and varied. There *is* dependency, yet he is very much a person in his own right. I'm glad he is here.

# 4. Other People

## People to Help

Whatever difficulties your child has, whether he was born with them or became disabled or handicapped later in life, there is a variety of services available to help you cope with your child's individual problems. These are based in health, education and social work or social service departments in each area but vary substantially depending on the priority afforded to services for handicapped children and adults by your own local authority.

The first person you will most likely come in contact with when you bring your baby home is the *health visitor*, who has special training with babies and young children. She should visit soon after you arrive home, and is a useful person to help you find out about your entitlement to disposable nappies for your disabled child, and also for large-size push-chairs which can be provided for growing children who have difficulty with moving about.

You may be lucky enough to have a group of *home visiting teachers* in your area and you should contact the education authorities to try and arrange for one to visit you on a regular basis as early as possible. Such a teacher will help you encourage the development of different functions with your child appropriate to his age and stage. The home visiting teacher is not there to test you or your child, only to encourage you to try out different things which you may not have thought of yourself. For children with hearing or sight difficulties, a home visiting teacher is invaluable in helping identify aids such as the phonic ear or radio hearing aid, or books with large type.

As a family with a disabled child you are entitled to a *social worker* who should be able to help you with the different benefits outlined in the previous chapter, and with other problems you may wish to discuss with her. When your child becomes sixteen he is then entitled to his own social worker. Social workers can help with placing children in residential homes where necessary and with arranging short-term relief if you need a break in caring for the sake of your own or your family's health. This can last from one day to several weeks, depending on the system in operation in your area. Social workers can also arrange holiday relief if you decide to go on holiday on your own or with your other children. Many areas have social workers who specialise in disability and physical handicap and have specialist and detailed knowledge and interest in this area.

For certain children, *physiotherapy* at the earliest possible stage is of crucial importance in the development of good posture, good toileting, and many important movement skills in future. Your family doctor or health visitor should be able to put you in touch with appropriate services in this area, or you may find that a physiotherapy service is available at your health centre.

Where communication and speech looks like being a problem contact with a *speech therapist* as early as possible is necessary for the development of good communication skills. Speech therapists do not deal only with speech defects such as stammers or burrs. They are communication specialists who can help a child with poor muscle control co-ordinate his speech abilities. For children who have no speech at all, they can pass on communication by sign systems such as Blissymbolics, which uses a specially-designed board with signs which the children point to, and Maketon, which is a simple sign language using either the left or right hand so that even severely handicapped children can manage it. The speech therapy services are administered by the health board, and can be contacted through the area or district health board office.

Disability is not an illness but it is important that your *family doctor* is fully aware of how your child's disability may affect diseases which he may contract. For instance if your child is on medication for epilepsy you may find that additional medication could upset the stability of the dosage for the epilepsy. It is important therefore for your family doctor to know your child's history. Your family doctor can be an invaluable ally in facilitating contact with other professionals.

Many areas have a *community nursing team* who deal specifically with handicapped people of all ages. The community nurse can help with providing equipment and aids, as well as by giving advice and having time to listen to any problems you or your family have. Again, your health board should have details of the provision in your area.

Still within the realms of the health board, your *dentist* is an important person to stay in touch with because of the extra damage that can be caused to the teeth of children who are on medication. The six-monthly check-up which is advised by dentists should be considered a priority where there may be risk to your child's dental health.

Although they have already been discussed, *teachers* and the education authorities must be included in any list of people to help. A variety of education staff are the main professional contact that most children will have for at least eleven years of their lives. A good parent-teacher relationship can bring only benefit to your child throughout the time he is going through the education system, keeping both you and the teacher informed and in touch with his progress.

Two other groups of people with whom you will come in contact during school years are the *educational psychologist* and *school medical officer*. They both play a large part in assessment procedures required for keeping the records up to date and can always be contacted if you feel you want to discuss any problems relating to your child's health or behaviour, having first talked with your own family doctor and teacher.

Many of the people working in the services are doing so under great pressure, trying to offer realistic help and advice to what may seem a huge client body. In these days of financial stringency and regional and national cutbacks many departments are not only unable to consider taking on additional workloads but are struggling even to maintain services to their existing clients.

Many voluntary workers from local associations of all kinds are available to help families with a disabled child. Central addresses are listed in the next section, and local addresses can be found in the Citizens' Advice Bureau or your local library.

One excellent service which is run on a non-profit-making basis is that of a taxi service for disabled children and adults. The name of this varies from area to area, but in general the name is a

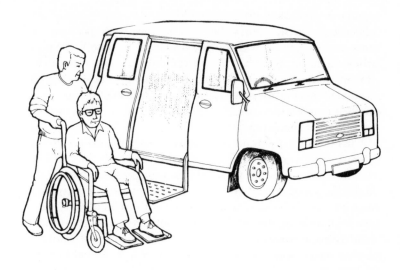

mixture of 'handicap' or 'disability' with 'taxi' or 'cab', such as 'Handicab'. This provides convenient transport arrangements at low cost for wheelchair users and people who are with them, but many have to be booked anything up to two or three weeks in advance.

## *Persistence and pressure*

While there is sympathy for the problems many professional people are facing, from a parent's point of view the services are in many cases inadequate and should be improved. Parents may find it difficult to make contact with people who can give useful aid and advice, and then have little faith in maintaining that contact. It is necessary to ask and keep on asking, time and time again. For many people this can be a daunting and disheartening prospect, and something which may seem like more trouble than it is worth. But things will not improve until parents and professionals identify the need for better services, and demand attention from the people with the power to change the existing services.

On the one hand parents are in the best possible position to pressurise and lobby for more services because they are the experts as far as their own children and their needs are concerned. On the other they are in the worst position — concerned as they are with the day-to-day issues of coping with a family including their handicapped child, they are often tired and in many cases disillusioned about the possibility of improvements in provision. However it is worth making even a small effort to make a case for the solution of any difficulty which you feel you are having.

The first point of contact you can make individually is with the professionals immediately involved with your own child. If you feel that you are getting no satisfaction, or not as much as you should be, you can contact the head of the relevant department. An approach to the local health council is also a valid and useful way to encourage the services to expand their provision. The health board in your own area will be able to furnish you with the name of the person you could contact if you want to make a case to them. You might also want to consider putting forward a member of your parents' group for election to the council so that you would have a permanent voice. Your health board will give you details of the date of the elections and appropriate procedures.

Local and regional councillors are there to try and meet the needs of the residents living in their area. Handicap is an emotional and sensitive subject however, and can easily become a 'political issue' because of the emotional blackmail which can be exerted. This is an ethical issue on which people have to satisfy their own conscience. If services are improved, do the needs justify the means? Having said that, many councillors offer valuable aid to many people in their area without being concerned about ensuring votes and may fail to offer a service only because they do not know that a need exists.

Parents' groups can form useful pressure groups, as many voices raised in unison always speak louder than one. As well as providing support and information, the group can act as a focus for a feature for local newspapers or local independent radio, both of whom are generally delighted to be approached by people who have a personal concern with local issues. The section in 'Finding Out More' on parents' groups outlines how to set up a group if there is not one already in your area.

# Communicating with the Services

As a parent you are the person who knows your own needs and those of your child. Professionals can advise and suggest various strategies but you have ultimately to make them work. It may be worthwhile considering a few points which may help cope with the knots in which bureaucratic red tape can become entangled.

## By phone

If you make a telephone call for instance, keep it as short as possible for your sake and for that of the person you are calling. Phones can distort your voice and many things which are said face to face with complete understanding run the risk of misinterpretation over the telephone where the people talking do not have non-verbal cues such as a smile or a nod of the head to help them fully understand. Even as a skilled telephone user there is a danger too that you may speak either too quietly or too loudly or hold the receiver too far away from your mouth because you may be anxious or very concerned about the issue to hand. This can be both disconcerting and uncomfortable for the person on the other end of the line.

Sometimes people overlook the fact that most professional people are not sitting in their offices twiddling their thumbs waiting for someone to phone them. A telephone call may interrupt a meeting or come at a time when they are dealing with something completely different from what the caller wants to talk about and it can be difficult to assemble all the relevant information immediately. So as well as feeling that they have been put on the spot slightly, they may not give you as much information as they actually have at their disposal.

## By letter

In order to overcome some of these difficulties a letter may often be a more effective means of communication. As well as providing a record in black and white of contact with any given division or person, a letter allows the recipient time to gather information, to concentrate on the questions posed, and to answer them in the most helpful and valuable way. For you as a person with an inquiry it is also helpful in clarifying your own thoughts, since writing something down helps you to put together clear questions. When you do write it is better to be as clear in your requests as possible so that the person you are actually writing to does not have to contact you, or consult a file, before being able to answer your query. A letter which asks 'I would like to know what services are available for my three-year-old child' could be more easily answered if the nature of the child's handicap and a specific request for speech therapy or physiotherapy were included. Always set a deadline in your own mind for when you want a reply, always allowing of course for time for postal collection and for the person to answer. That way there is no danger of your letter being forgotten under a pile of books, or put aside. It is a simple matter too to jog someone's conscience by a note saying 'I assume my last letter has got lost in the post'. In this way the blame is apportioned to some unfortunate faceless 'system' rather than being laid directly at someone's feet — which does nothing for good communication.

## *In a meeting*

As your child grows up you will meet professionals both individually and in groups, and there are some points worth remembering which can help carry you through some of the more important and therefore tense situations in which you may find yourself. Some people do not mind speaking in a group where they do not know anyone particularly well, but some people find it quite a nerve-racking business, especially where important decisions are being made which will affect the future of their own child. Sitting back in your chair with your hands folded in your lap helps you feel more relaxed, and licking your lips before you speak will help prevent that horrible feeling of a dry mouth which many people experience when anxious. Try and become conscious of tension in your shoulder muscles which can make you look hunched up, or in your legs which will make you cross your legs once or even twice, and in your whole body which will make you sit forward on the edge of your chair. Notice

too any little tics or nervous habits which will tell other people
you are anxious, like rubbing your nose or twisting a ring round
your finger. By looking calm you will show that you are in charge
of the situation and that your opinion is of value.

## *Keeping note*

From the very first time you have contact with any professional
after you have been told that your child has a difficulty or
disability, it is advisable to keep a note of all contacts so that you
have a clear record of everything that has happened from the
beginning. All you need to do is jot down the date of every
telephone call and with whom you spoke, every visit to a doctor
or hospital, every visit made by a health visitor, home teacher, or
social worker, and of course keep a copy of every letter you write,
and every one you receive. It all sounds a fuss and bother but you
will be thankful you did so if anything ever goes wrong.

## *Parents as experts*

There are lots of professional people and services available for
your support and help. You may find that you have to keep
going back to the same people apparently asking for the same
things over and over again. You may feel that you are being a
bother. But ultimately you are the expert as far as your child is
concerned, and you have both the right and the duty to make as
much use of the services for the benefit of yourself, your family
and your special child.

# **People to Hinder?**

People have funny attitudes to disability and handicap, and this
in turn means unfortunately that there are strange attitudes to
those with some kind of disability. There has always been
handicap and there always will be, but what most people
concerned with disability want is that it be accepted as a normal
part of human life, and that people with disability should not be
separate from the 'normal' population.

Nowadays children in special education are called children with special needs, or children with learning difficulties. They used to be categorised according to their type of handicap — mentally handicapped, physically handicapped — but professions involved with special care recognised that many of these labels set children apart and made them in some way different from other children. By using these labels inappropriately, people were losing sight of the child and were reacting only to his or her handicap.

We all have labels, some of which stay the same all our lives, and some of which change as we grow up. When used correctly labels can be useful — say, for instance, for identifying who is the receptionist and who is the doctor. Some labels help us build our self-image and self-esteem — if other people treat us as someone with a 'nice' label we tend to act that way. However, some labels are perceived by other people as 'good' labels and some as 'bad' or undesirable labels, such as 'handicapped'. Because of fear, embarrassment or a lack of understanding, many people could not — cannot — see the person behind the label. In recent years however there have been the beginnings of a slow change. A government report called *Special Educational Needs* published in 1978 recommended that the specific categories of handicap be discarded.

## *Integration and normalisation*

One of the other major recommendations in *Special Educational Needs* was that children with special educational needs be integrated where possible. In that report, integration was defined at three levels: 'locational' integration, where disabled and non-disabled children were educated or housed in the same premises; 'social' integration, where they mixed together in their free time; and 'functional' integration, where all childen were educated together, and ate and played together. Such emphasis on integration — and the debate raged loud and long — led to the principle and philosophy of 'normalisation', often confused with 'making normal' — whatever 'normal' is. It is a reality which has to be accepted that children with mental, physical or sensory handicaps will always have those difficulties to deal with.

No amount of special exercises or structured training will cause new brain cells to grow or impaired limbs to reform. What special training is invaluable for is aiding the child to develop to his or her full potential as a person with different skills and abilities. And it is the recognition of the disabled child or adult as a valued person with such skills that normalisation refers to. In other words, what people concerned with disability are looking towards is a broader definition of 'normality' to include disabled and handicapped people as accepted members of the community, with a valid contribution to make.

Social attitudes however do not change overnight, and prejudices rooted in superstition and ignorance over centuries are particularly resistant. The International Year of Disabled People in 1981 went some way towards raising awareness that people's attitudes could do with reappraisal. By putting the question 'Can Disabled People Go Where You Go?' the organisers forced an awareness that many shop doors were too narrow for even a child's wheelchair, or too heavy for someone

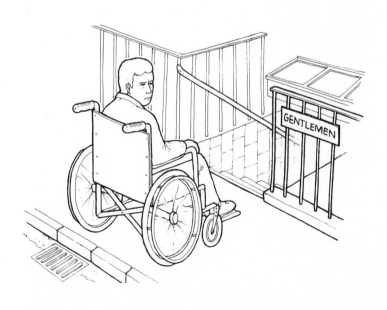

to open while pushing a chair or walking with aids. Many other environmental anomalies were highlighted, for instance no access by ramps into many public buildings, no ramps at pedestrian crossings, or, even worse, a ramp at one side of the road but not on the other. IYDP 1981 also saw the appointment of Access Officers in each area, who oversee access facilities in new and existing buildings. A step in the right direction — but not all handicapped children are in a wheelchair.

Much public education is required in this area. Children with disabilities grow up into adults with disabilities, and at all times deserve the dignity of being a person first and foremost. A press and poster campaign begun in 1981 shows a young man in a wheelchair with the slogan 'Try treating everyone the same'. Several follow-up publications for parents of handicapped children and for relatives and friends have reinforced this philosophy.

Television has done much towards public education by broadcasting both feature items and complete programmes on various aspects of handicap and disability in documentaries and even by creating characters with some type of handicap in long-established soap operas. Television is one of the most powerful media, since it allows people to 'stand and stare' at a child or adult with a disability without the social embarrassment which would be caused if the person was there in the situation. By looking and listening to the facts of disability presented in an informative and interesting way in their own living-room where they do not feel awkward or shy, people are more willing to consider and revaluate their own attitudes to disabled people when they come into direct contact with them.

Families and individuals too can do a great deal in helping to change social attitudes by making sure that a child, no matter what his or her handicap or disability, with whatever kind of aids, takes a proper place in the family, not as the centre of attraction but as an ordinary member with an equal part to play. By taking your child out with you and encouraging him to do what you would do with any other child, you are helping other people to realise that disabled children are children first — children who have some kind of disability.

People may stare, they may mutter 'What a shame', they may

react in any one of a hundred ways. They may feel embarrassed by a child wearing some kind of aid — *but that is their inadequacy.*

Trying to *hide* a disability by cosmetic surgery or by uncomfortable or unhealthy clothing only erodes and destroys a child's self-esteem and confidence by trying to ignore something that is part of him as a person. *Camouflage* of an aid or an impairment — by having a pinafore or dungarees with a front pocket for a hearing-impaired child using a radio aid or a phonic ear — can save curiosity, and can enhance children's confidence to participate to the best of their abilities in what is going on around them.

# 5. Finding Out More

Whenever anything of fairly long-term proportions comes into a person's life, after the initial reaction most of us need and want to find out more information about how to cope with the new conditions in the best way possible. Many people who have recovered from illness want to know more about their disease. Many disabilities or impairments are not diseases and children and adults who are disabled or handicapped are generally not ill. They are normal, healthy human beings who have difficulties to a degree which the majority of people do not experience.

Nevertheless, as the parent of a handicapped child, you will probably still want to find out as much as possible about your youngster's condition so that you can do what is best for him, and understand and come to terms with the effects of his particular — and individual — difficulties. There are services who should be available to talk to you and discuss any points you wish to raise, but they are pressurised, under-staffed and under-funded. However several other sources of information are available.

## Voluntary Organisations

Ideally voluntary and statutory services should complement each other and work together. Like most things, in some areas they do, and in some they do not. Different voluntary organisations provide different kinds of services. Some provide local group meetings and clubs, newsletters and publications, while some promote research, or co-ordinate schools, sheltered employment, accommodation facilities and longterm care.

One thing for sure is that like all interested professional people in the statutory sector, those people working in the voluntary organisations always welcome inquiries from people looking for information and help, and always welcome contact with people with experience and skills which they can share.

The following list of organisations is not exhaustive and many of the national bodies have local branches. Not all of them will satisfy your individual needs but by contacting the head office you will be able to identify more clearly just what any one organisation offers.

## Accommodation

L'Arche UK
14 London Road
Beccles
Suffolk NR34 9NH
0502 713329

Sheltered accommodation for mentally handicapped young people and adults.

## Adventure Playgrounds for Handicapped Children

Handicapped Adventure
Playgrounds Assoc.
Fulham Palace
Bishops Avenue
London SW6 6EA
01-736 4443

Advice and information
Films and equipment details.

## Autism

National Autistic Society
276 Willesden Lane
London NW2 5RB
01-451 3844/5

Information and material for parents and professionals. Twice-yearly conferences. Quarterly newsletter.

## Blindness

National Association for
Deaf, Blind & Rubella
Handicapped
311 Gray's Inn Road
London WC1X 8PT
01-278 1005

Advice and information to parents. Local groups. Quarterly newsletter. Books, leaflets and films.

The Royal Blind Asylum
& School
Gillespie Crescent
Edinburgh EH10 4H2
031-229 1456

Educational facilities.
Information for parents.

Royal National Institute
for the Blind
224 Great Portland Street
London W1N 6AA
01-388 1266

Braille publications.
Schools, holiday and hostel
facilities. Monthly
publication.

## Brain Damage

National Society for Brain
Damaged Children
35 Larchmere Drive
Birmingham B28 8JB
021-777 4284

Centre providing assessment
and techniques for home
therapy.

## Brittle Bones

Brittle Bone Society
112 City Road
Dundee DD2 2PW
0382 67603

Help and advice for sufferers
of osteogenesis imperfecta.
Fund raising.

## Care Attendant Schemes

Association of Crossroads
Care Attendant Schemes Ltd
94a Coton Road
Rugby
Warwickshire CV21 3AY
0788 61536

Home relief and personal
care services by trained
assistants for severely
disabled people.

## Cerebral Palsy

Scottish Council for Spastics
22 Corstorphine Road
Edinburgh EH12 6HP
031-337 9876

Schools, sheltered workshops.
Advice & information for
parents.

The Spastics Society
12 Park Crescent
London W1N 4BQ
01-636 5020

Schools, residential facilities
advice and information for
parents, counselling.
Publications.

## Contact a Family

Contact a Family
16 Strutton Ground
Victoria
London SW1P 2HP
01-222 2695

Local self-help family groups.

## Crippling Diseases

Action Research for the
Crippled Child
(National Fund for Research
into Crippling Diseases)
Vincent House
Springfield Road
Horsham, W Sussex
0403 64101

Promotes and supports
research.
Quarterly journal.

## Cystic Fibrosis

Cystic Fibrosis Research
Trust
5 Blyth Road
Bromley
Kent BR1 3RS
01-464 7211

Finances research.
Newsletter.

## Deafness

British Deaf Association
38 Victoria Place
Carlisle CA1 1HU
0228 20188

Local branches. Advice on
education and development.
Educational material &
bi-monthly magazine.

National Deaf Children's
Society
45 Hereford Road
London W2 5AN
01-229 9272

Advice to parents; home
assistant schemes for families
with a deaf child. Courses;
holiday scheme.
Quarterly newsletter.

Royal National Institute
for the Deaf
105 Gower Street
London WC1E 6AH
01-387 8033

Residential homes and
hostels.
Information on deafness, aids
etc.
Newsletters & journal.

See also under **Blindness**.

## Diabetes

British Diabetic Association
10 Queen Anne Street
London W1M 0RD
01-323 1531

Information and advice for
sufferers. Fund raising.
Organises holidays for
diabetic children. Bi-monthly
newsletter.

## Disability

Disability Alliance
25 Denmark Street
London WC2H 8NJ
01-240 0806

Information on welfare
rights. Conferences and
research pamphlets. Bulletins
and handbook.

Reach — The Association for Children with Artificial Arms
11 Shelley Road
St Marks, Cheltenham
Gloucestershire
0242 36552

Advice and counselling for parents.
Self-help groups.

Scottish Council on Disability
Princes House
5 Shandwick Place
Edinburgh
031-229 8632

Information and advice for parents and all disabled people.

Wales Council for the Disabled
Llys Ifor, Crescent Road
Caerphilly
Midglamorgan CF8 1XL
0222 869224

Advice and information to parents and sufferers.
Publications.

### Disabled, Riding for the

Riding for the Disabled Association
National Agricultural Centre
(Avenue R), Kenilworth
Warwickshire CV8 2LY
0203 56107

Local groups throughout the U.K.

### Disfigurement

Society of Skin Camouflage
Disfigurement Guidance Centre
150 High Street
Newburgh
Fife
03372 8190

Advice and counselling.
Information on special treatments.
Bulletin.

## Dr Barnardo's

Dr Barnardo's
Tanners Lane
Barkingside, Ilford
Essex 1G6 1QG
01-550 8822

Schools and day care centres.

## Downs Syndrome

Downs Children's
Association
4 Oxford Street
London W1
01-580 0511/2

Advice and help for parents.

## Dyslexia

British Dyslexia Association
Linton Place, Church Lane
Peppard
Oxon
649 17 699

Local associations. Research.

## Eczema

National Eczema Society
Tavistock House North
Tavistock Square
London WC1H 9SR
01-388 4097

Local groups. Publications on
eczema.
Quarterly newsletter.

## Epilepsy

British Epilepsy Association
Crowthorne House
New Wokingham Road
Wokingham
Berkshire RG11 3AY
034 46 3122

Courses and seminars. Films/
tape service. Research.
Holidays.

Scottish Epilepsy Association
48 Govan Road
Glasgow
041-427 4911

Advice and information for
parents and sufferers.
Sheltered workshops.

## Family Fund

Family Fund
Joseph Rowntree
Memorial Trust, PO Box 50
York YD1 1UY
0904-21115

Fund to help families with
severely disabled children
under 16. Help can be goods,
services or cash for some
definite purpose.

## Friedreich's Ataxia

Friedreich's Ataxia Group
12c Worplesdon Road
Guildford, Surrey
0483 503133

Advice and information.
Fund raising.
Quarterly newsletter.

## Gingerbread

Gingerbread
35 Wellington Street
London WC2
01-240 0953

Help and advice for single
parents.
Local groups.

## Girl Guides

The Girl Guides Association
17-19 Buckingham Palace Rd
London SW1W 0PP
01-834 6242

Leisure activities and
interests.
Social activities for
handicapped children.

## Haemophilia

Haemophilia Society
PO Box 9
16 Trinity Street
London SE1 1DE
01-407 1010

Local groups. Advice and
information.

## Handicapped Children

Voluntary Council for
Handicapped Children
National Children's Bureau
8 Wakeley Street
London EC1V 7QE
01-278 9441

Seminars and workshops.
Information service to
voluntary organisations and
professionals. Newsletter,
books for parents.

## Health Education

Health Education Council
78 New Oxford Street
London WC1A 1AH
01-637 1881

Information on all aspects of
health.

Scottish Health Education
Group
Woodburn House
Canaan Lane
Edinburgh EH10 4SG
031-447 8044

Information on all aspects
of health.

## Hospital Care

National Association for the
Welfare of Children
in Hospital
Argyle House
29-31 Euston Road
London NW1 2SD
01-833 2641

Information and counselling
service. Arranges play
and transport schemes for
wards.
Conferences, local meetings.

## Huntington's Chorea

Association to Combat
Huntington's Chorea
Lyndhurst
Lower Hampton Road
Sunbury on Thames
Middlesex TW16 5PR
01-979 5055

Help for sufferers and their
relatives.
Explanatory booklets.

## Hydrocephalus — See **Spina Bifida**

## In Touch Scheme

The In Touch Scheme
Ann Worthington
10 Norman Road
Sale, Cheshire M33 3DF
061-962 4441

Advice and help for parents
of handicapped children.
Self help groups.

## Invalid Children's Aid

Invalid Children's Aid
Association
126 Buckingham Palace Rd
London SW1W 9SB
01-730 9891

Advice and help for parents.
Four residential schools.
Publications and films.

## Kith and Kids

Kith and Kids
c/o Helen Berent
Bedford House
35 Emerald Street
London WC1
01-504 3001

Self-help advice for parents of
handicapped children.

## Leukaemia

Leukaemia Research Fund
43 Great Ormond Street
London WC1N 3JJ
01-405 0101

Funds research.

Leukaemia Society
P.O. Box 82
Exeter
EX2 5DP

Information, support,
financial help and holidays.

## Mental Handicap

Association of Professions for
the Mentally Handicapped
King's Fund Centre
126 Albert Street
London NW1 7NF
01-267 6111

Local group meetings and
information on many aspects
of mental handicap.
Quarterly newsletter.

MENCAP
123 Golden Lane
London EC1Y 0RT
01-253 9433

Support and advice to
parents. Local groups.
Conferences.
Publications.

Scottish Society for the
Mentally Handicapped
13 Elmbank Street
Glasgow G2 4RA
041-226 4541

Advice and information for
parents; housing association;
publications.

### Mobility

Motability
Boundary House
91-93 Charterhouse Street
London EC1
01-253 1211

Advises people on mobility,
and can organise vehicle
purchase using mobility
allowance.

### Multiple Sclerosis

Arms (Action for Research
into Multiple Sclerosis)
71 Grays Inn Road
London WC1X 8TR
01-568 2255

Fund raising and research.
Information.

Multiple Sclerosis Society of
Great Britain and Northern
Ireland
286 Munster Road
London SW6 6AP
01-381 4022/4025 or
01-385 6146/7/8

Fund raising, local
associations, holiday and
short stay homes.

### Muscular Dystrophy

Muscular Dystrophy Group
of Great Britain
Nattrass House
35 Macaulay Road
London SW4 0QP
01-720 8055

Fund raising, local groups.
Publications.

**Parents' Groups** — See

**Contact a Family**
**Gingerbread**
**In Touch Scheme**
**Kith and Kids**

## Phenylketonuria

National Society for
Phenylketonuria & Allied
Disorders
26 Towngate Grove
Mirfield
West Yorkshire
0924 492873

Fund raising, research,
conferences.
Provision of holiday homes.

## Physically Disabled Children

Lady Hoare Trust for
Physically Disabled Children
7 North Street
Midhurst,
West Sussex GU29 9DJ
073 081 3696

Comprehensive social work/
welfare support system.

Physically Handicapped &
Able Bodied (PHAB)
Tavistock House North
Tavistock Square
London WC1H 9HX
01-388 6433

Local groups organise social
and leisure activities.

**Playgrounds** — See

**Adventure Playgrounds for**
**Handicapped Children**

## Polio

British Polio Fellowship
Bell Close, West End Road
Ruislip
Middlesex HA4 6LP
089 56 75515

Training in occupations.
Hostels and workshop
schemes.
Quarterly publication.

## Renal Conditions

Renal Society
64 South Hill Park
London NW3 2SJ
01-794 9479

Newsletter provides contact
and information on diets and
possible sources of financial
help to kidney patients.

## Restricted Growth

Association for Research into
Restricted Growth
8 Herbert Road
Clevedon
Avon BS21 7ND
0272 877243

Fund raising and promotion
of research.
Information.

## Retinitis Pigmentosa

British Retinitis Pigmentosa
Society
Secretary:
Mrs LM Drummond-Walker
24 Palmer Close
Redhill
Surrey
0737 61937

Information and advice.
Fund raising.
Quarterly newsletter.

**Riding for the Disabled** — See **Disabled, Riding for the**

**Rubella** — See under **Blindness**

**Sheltered Accommodation** — See **Accommodation**

**Single Parents** — See **Gingerbread**

**Skin Camouflage** — See **Disfigurement**

## Speech Impairment

Association for All Speech
Impaired Children (AFASIC)
347 Central Markets
Smithfield
London EC1
01-236 3632/6487

Advice and information.

## Spina Bifida

Association for Spina Bifida
and Hydrocephalus
22 Upper Woburn Place
London WC1H 0EP
01-388 1382

Local branches. Advice and
support service.
Supports research.
Bi-monthly magazine.

Scottish Spina Bifida
Association
190 Queensferry Road
Edinburgh EH4 2BW
031-332 0743

Advice and information for
parents, counselling.

### Spinal Injuries

Spinal Injuries Association
Yeoman House
76 St. James's Lane
London N10 3DF
01-444 2121

Advice and information to
sufferers and their relatives.
Quarterly newsletters.

### Vaccine Damage

Association of Parents of
Vaccine Damaged Children
2 Church Street
Shipston-on-Stour
Warwickshire CV36 4AP
0608-61595

Information and help for
parents.

# Parents' Groups

Another good way of finding out about services in your area is to
join a parents' group. There are several of these about and you
should be able to find out where they meet from your library,
your social worker or home visiting teacher. Most people find
that joining a group helps them come to terms with their disabled
child. They find emotional support and friendship among
people who really understand the problems they face and the
different situations in which they find themselves. At first you
may not feel ready to talk openly about your child, or you may
feel shy or lacking in confidence about going along to a group
whose members will seem to know each other while you know
nobody. It may be helpful to consider having a word beforehand
with the group organiser so that at least you will know one
person.

## Starting a group

There is a great need for more of these groups. There may not be one in your area or the existing group may be fairly large. Starting a group like this can be a lot of hard work but very rewarding. You may already know a few people who would be interested in forming a group and a short letter inviting them along to an initial meeting will set the ball rolling. If each person then brings a new member at further meetings, the group will grow quite quickly and naturally.

Finding a place to meet can often be a tricky business. Many church halls or schools are available in the evenings but have to be paid for to fund heating and lighting costs and the overtime of the janitor. However it is worthwhile checking these places out since voluntary groups such as parents' groups are often entitled to reduced charges. It is often more comfortable to meet in people's homes, even if it means a bit of a crush. Taking it in turns spreads the load of providing coffee and biscuits and clearing up afterwards.

Deciding on the time to meet is the next consideration and this can be most difficult since everybody has different commitments. It may be more convenient to meet during the day and organise crèche facilities by each member of the group taking a turn to watch the children. Inevitably it has to be a compromise to suit the majority of members.

Having got a group together, it can be difficult to strike a happy balance between too much formality and too little structure. Both can put people off coming to meetings. However with some forward planning members can know in advance what they are committed to. Many people such as social workers or voluntary workers are available to come and talk to groups, although it can be a good idea to give the speaker perhaps only thirty minutes to talk and allow thirty minutes for discussion. Always set some time aside for socialising — this is an important function of a group like this. A film too can be a good way to start a meeting. Many are now available on video-cassette and can be used by families who have home video facilities. Home videos come in two different formats, VHS and Betamax, and when you are hiring you should state which you require as VHS does not fit Betamax video-recorders and vice versa. There is a short selected list of firms and videos on page 84.

## Sharing responsibility

One of the inevitable risks of starting a parents' group is that you will be left to do all the work, ordering films or videos, and inviting speakers. It often needs one person to get a group off the ground but once it is established it is important that several, if not all, of the group members share the tasks involved. Apart from the obvious benefit this has to the person in danger of being landed with all the work, sharing the load helps each person feel more committed to taking part in what is going on and feel more part of a specific and identifiable group. It is important for the success of activities and functions run by a parents' group that each member feels committed to making it work.

# Literature

There are many interesting and helpful books on all aspects of handicap and disability. The following is only a short selection of the vast number available. Your library or newsletters from some voluntary organisations will keep you up to date on what is new.

*Directory for the Disabled*, Darnbrough and Kinrade, published by Woodhead Faulkner (1977), gives a comprehensive list of organisations dealing with a wide variety of topics, including housing, equipment, aids, leisure activities, holidays, employment and legislation.

*Helping Your Handicapped Baby*, Cunningham & Sloper, published by Souvenir Press (1978), provides exercises and games to help a young handicapped child go through the early stages of development.

*Kith and Kids*, Maurice & Doreen Collins, published by Souvenir Press (1976), is a self-help guide for families of a handicapped child and is the story of how one family set up a self-help group in their own area.

*Coming to Terms with Mental Handicap*, Ann Worthington, published by Helena Press (1982), explores parental feelings and reactions to the birth of a handicapped baby and the early years.

*Handicapped at Home*, Sydney Foott, published by the Design Centre (1977), gives advice on the planning, design and choice of equipment for use in a home with a disabled person.

*Getting The Best For Your Child* is a free publication available only in Scotland from the Scottish Health Education Group which gives information to parents on benefits, statutory and voluntary organisations, and educational and social facilities in Scotland for children with all disabilities.

*Sixteen — And Then What?*, Andrina E McCormack, published by Helena Press (1984), explores the future for mentally impaired adults, their housing, employment and education needs, and leisure activities, as well as giving a comprehensive and international list of organisations for handicapped people.

# Microprocessors

As well as there being books and audiovisual material which you can use in your own home, the technological revolution has changed our lives extensively and offered us the possibility of having a microprocessor or microcomputer in our own living room. An increasing amount of software is available in the area of disability and while you may feel that your children are more adept with the micro than you are, it can be very rewarding to familiarise yourself with its use. Popular print material and many magazines are available at the local newsagent on a weekly or monthly basis.

Several projects have been set up to provide a database in special needs, and access to these is available both to parents and professionals. These are based in five centres in the UK.

Special Educational Needs Information Exchange Project (SEND)
Scottish Council for Educational Technology
74 Victoria Crescent Road
Glasgow
041-334 9314

Special Educational Microelectronics Resource Centre
(SEMERC)
Newcastle Polytechnic
Coach Lane Campus
Newcastle Upon Tyne
0632 665057

SEMERC
Manchester College of Higher Education
Hathersage Road
Manchester
061-225 9054

SEMERC
Faculty of Education
Bristol Polytechnic
Redland Hill
Bristol
0272 741251

SEMERC
Grange Remedial Centre
Woodman Path
Hainault
Ilford
01-500 8092

# Spreading the Word

People who are closely involved with the many issues
surrounding disability recognise the crucial problems which
require solution. To others, with no direct experience in this
area, these questions may not warrant even passing notice.
Through the media, press and television, however, more people
are coming into closer contact with handicapped children and
adults and as a result of this they want more information about
the experience of disability or impairment. This can be seen only
as a good thing — the more people *know* the less they *imagine*.

Many schools are including education about disability in their social education or guidance slots with teenagers in the mainstream sector. With the integration of children with disabilities into ordinary schools all pupils need to be made aware of situations which might cause problems for a disabled child. For instance, they need to be encouraged to remember always to face a person with partial hearing when they are in conversation — and to remember to speak clearly but not to shout!

Community groups too are becoming interested in disability because of the increasing numbers of group homes or sheltered flats based in local areas. Church groups, women's guilds and Rotary Clubs are always keen to hear of new areas in which they can take an interest.

You may as a parent be willing to make it known that you would speak to these community groups or school classes about your own experience in this area. For some people it can be a frightening thought to stand up in front of a group and be the centre of attention. Others really enjoy it and take to it like ducks to water. But no amount of films, books or leaflets can substitute for someone talking about his or her own personal experience in a sensitive and factual way — you do not have to bare your soul.

# Films and Video Material

There are several films and videotapes which can be used to start off or augment a session with an interested group, and of course they are always of great use to a parents' group in helping them focus attention on a given issue, or in providing direction or structure for a meeting.

The following are available from the Central Film Library:

*Don't Shout — I'm Deaf* is for all those who are likely to come in contact with hearing impaired people in their work. The package gives information and advice on the problems of deafness and includes a 16 mm film, tape/slide set and teaching notes.

*So We're Different But...* looks at the way teachers and therapists cope with a wide range of physically disabled children and help them integrate into mainstream schools (16 mm).

*Unseen Hazards* portrays many of the hazards blind people encounter every day. The film outlines how sighted people can help (16 mm).

Available from the BBC:

*Accident of Birth* which aims to stress the difference between people who are mentally ill and those who are mentally handicapped (16 mm/video).

*Our Peter* is about a fourteen-year-old boy's struggle to overcome huge physical disabilities (16 mm).

*James Is Our Brother* presents the home life of a family with a Down's Syndrome teenager (16 mm/video).

Available from the Scottish Central Film Library:

*Getting the Best For Your Child: The Early Years, Play* emphasises the importance of play for the young handicapped child, shows exercises and outlines services, such as parents' groups, toy libraries and various professionals which help (video).

*The Truly Exceptional Dan Haley* is a moving account of one teenager's fight against progressive blindness (16 mm).

*The Truly Exceptional Carol Johnston* shows a teenager with one arm, who trains for the national gymnastic competition which she ultimately wins (16 mm).

*Mental Handicap — A Social View* outlines social attitudes to mental handicap (video and material). This is also available from Graves Medical Audio Visual Library.

The Mental Health Film Council at 22 Harley Street, London (01-637 0741) has a very comprehensive catalogue of films and video material. Other useful addresses are:

Central Film Library
Chalfont Grove
Gerrards Cross
Bucks
02407 4111

BBC Enterprises Ltd Film Hire
Woodston House
Dundee Road
Peterborough
0733 32257/8

Concord Film Council
201 Felixstowe Road
Ipswich
0473 715754

Scottish Central Film Library
74 Victoria Crescent Road
Glasgow
041-334 9314

Graves Medical Audio Visual Library
220 New London Road
Chelmsford
0245 83351

By gathering as much knowledge, promoting research and spreading information by all means possible — word of mouth, the written word, film, video, television and radio — those concerned with disability and handicap are giving the general public, which includes parents and professionals, the opportunity to broaden their knowledge about disability, broaden the concept of normality to include as wide a range of people as possible, and to see and treat other people the way they like to be treated themselves.

# 6. Looking Ahead

The birth of a handicapped baby is not what parents plan for. Disablement through illness or accident is something which most parents, consciously or otherwise, fear for their child. Improved ante-natal services help to reduce the numbers of children born with a handicap by early identification of any problems. Safe and more sensitive conditions during labour and birth further enhance the chances of babies who may have been at risk in the past. Immunisation against rubella (German measles) helps reduce the number of children born handicapped through rubella damage.

But no matter how many improvements are made, there will always be people who are impaired, disabled or handicapped in some way.

Some people will be more physically disabled than others, some will be more mentally or sensorily handicapped than others. Without minimising the difficulties which many disabled people experience and the problems which face parents of children who are disabled, we can say that there are always people who are better and worse at what we do and are ourselves.

It can sound a very trite philosophy, but peeling back the top layer you find the principles and philosophies of community care, integration and normalisation embodied in the statement Think Ability, Not Disability.

We have talked for years of 'the blind', 'the deaf', 'the handicapped', forgetting that these are *people* first. We talk now about depersonalisation, socialisation, normalisation.

Maybe we should be thinking about a new -isation for future development and progress. Could it be *humanisation*?